Ĵ FIC
BAR

Barlow, Eleanor Poe.
The master's cat.

$24.00

DATE			

THE MASTER'S CAT

THE MASTER'S CAT

The Story of Charles Dickens as told by his Cat

ELEANOR POE BARLOW

THE DICKENS HOUSE, LONDON

First published 1998 by
Dickens Publishing for the Dickens House,
48 Doughty Street, London, WC1N 2LF

British Library Cataloguing in Publication Data
A catalogue record for this book is available from the
British Library

ISBN 0-9518525-3-1

Typeset by Scribe Design, Gillingham, Kent
Printed in the UK by The Lavenham Press, Suffolk

Contents

For my dear Mother and Father
Eleanor and Joel Barlow
who believed in this book
and have always believed in me.

List of Illustrations

Illustrations are reproduced by courtesy of The Dickens House Museum, London

LIST OF ILLUSTRATIONS

List of Illustrations

LIST OF ILLUSTRATIONS

Acknowledgements

A lone person may write a book, but a host sees to its publication. to that host I am deeply grateful.

First in its rank is CEDRIC CHARLES DICKENS. He fired the enterprise with his eager response to my idea, and he brought it to completion by initiating and coordinating the process of publication. He is a tireless editor and agent as well as a cherished friend.

CAROLINE SEAMANS, Head of St. Peter's School, Philadelphia, not only gave me free rein to write a curriculum that made Dickens and other literary greats the intimates of young people, she found the resources to implement that curriculum. Her support in spirit and in action has made the dream of this book a reality.

PROFESSOR ELLIOTT ENGEL, international literary speaker who presides over the largest branch of The Dickens Fellowship in the world (7,000 members) spurred me on with his own enthusiasm and with generous grants from that Fellowship.

ANN EVERITT, Headmistress of Gad's Hill School, enabled me to know the home of Master and Cat by welcoming me, not once but twice, to teach in the fine school she has made.

ALISON SAMPH transcribed my pencilled pages into flawless elegant manuscript, thereby giving me early pride in authorship.

And when I nearly lost that manuscript to the mysteries of word processing, it was PAULA PAWKA who retrieved it and saved me!

And a whole host of friends I have yet to meet MICHAEL ROGERS, Head of English at King's College, Taunton. Dr DAVID PARKER, Curator of the Dickens House Museum, and especially ANDREW XAVIER and BRIAN PERKINS of Dickens House and JUNE CUMMINGS and all her friends who have made the book a reality. Bless them all.

In the goodly fellowship that is teaching and learning I was blessed with COLLEAGUES, STUDENTS and THEIR PARENTS who brought me books and all things Dickensian. Their eagerness to know Charles Dickens inspired me.

Eleanor Poe Barlow
Friendship
Maine
October 30, 1997

Introduction

I count myself lucky to be one of a happy band of people who encouraged my dear friend, Poesy, to spend a short part of a summer term at Gad's Hill School, and afterwards to lay before her small threads of attractive material which she has woven so beautifully into this book.

Whenever I walk through the front door of Gad's Hill I enter another world – a happy world with the whisper of childish laughter and the patter of small feet in the background.

It is so easy to imagine that I will find my great-grandfather sitting at his desk, busy with his quill pens, muttering to himself as his characters dictate their parts, and the small kitten watching every movement.

And then again, off he goes, on his rounds of inspection and repair, with the dogs and cat gambolling about him. A tour of his boundary, through the stables and under the tunnel, excavated in the days of the horse, carriage and cart, long before there was any heavy traffic, and so well built that it withstood the ravages of time in these hectic days!

The chalet is no longer in the Wilderness; but it can be seen, not far away, in the Rochester to which Gad's Hill Place really belongs.

My dear friend, Poesy, has brought it all to life for me in this little book. I am so thrilled that I discovered her at St Peter's School in Philadelphia many years ago when I used to spend the odd hour early in the morning with her English Class talking about Gad's Hill and the country-side around – especially the Marshes of *Great Expectations*. They are there yet: time has stood still for them.

The study which was the heart of the house in HIS day is still the heart of the school with headmistress presiding!

It is still very much as he left it, with the fireplace, desk (reproduction), dummy books and mirrors, and indeed the shelves all around full of old books. There he sits, at his desk, in the bay window, his pen moving rapidly across the paper, his characters dancing on its tip demanding he tells their stories. So well did he do it that they are still with us. So well did he do it that he still lives, larger than life perhaps; but he still was very much a man.

Poesy's story through the voice of his little furry friend will, I know, give a lot of pleasure to generations of readers – perhaps showing him to be the man he was when he achieved his long awaited ambition of being the owner of a little bit of the Kent he loved.

Thank you Poesy.

Cedric Charles Dickens
Friday 19 December 1997

Author's Preface

Charles Dickens lived a life as fascinating as that of any character he created. It was full of sadness and joy, poverty and wealth, mystery and fame.

As a sickly boy of twelve, Dickens was forced to work in a rat-ridden factory to earn money to free his family from a debtors' prison. By a twist of fate, he became a writer instead of an actor. He was the proud father of ten children, but he shocked England by separating from their mother. When he became famous, he lived at the centre of a glittering London circle of writers and artists; but in his last troubled years, he found peace in the quiet Gad's Hill circle of his family and animals. Gad's Hill Place was the country estate he bought in 1856, and it was there that he died in 1870.

Gad's Hill Place from the front

In the last years Charles Dickens had a little four-footed companion, a deaf cat, who sat with him when he wrote and followed him wherever he went – around the house and on walks about his property and the countryside. Even worthier of note was this little creature's curious habit of putting out candles. We know about this loyal and clever cat because Dickens's children wrote about him: Mary, or Mamie as she was called, in her two books, *My Father as I Recall Him* and *Charles Dickens by His Eldest Daughter*, and Sir Henry Fielding Dickens in his book, *Memoirs of My Father*. Wherever the story can be told by Mamie or Sir Henry, I have let them do it.

I have chosen to introduce Charles Dickens to you through the eyes of his cat because his affection for the man should endear the author to you. He can tell you the great man's story filled with the daily doings and adventures of children and pets. He can also persuade his beloved master to go back in time and tell his own story.

Wherever possible I have given Charles Dickens his own words to speak. I have also given his words as found in letters, in his books, and in his autobiographical fragment to the cat in his descriptions of Gad's Hill, its family, its animals, and the habits of its master. This is to put you, my readers, as close as is possible to Charles Dickens. I have done this

The Study

with the encouragement of Cedric Charles Dickens, great grandson of Charles Dickens and grandson of Sir Henry. Cedric set his family biographies before me at his home in Somerset, England, on a summer day in 1992. I had come fresh from two weeks of teaching at Gad's Hill School on a grant from the Dickens Fellowship.

Gad's Hill School? Yes, Charles Dickens's house is a school. It was there, amidst lessons and laughter, that this book was born. I walked the gardens and meadows where Dickens and his cat walked. I sat in the Study where Dickens wrote his last four books, his dear companion curled beside him. I felt close to them both and wanted to bring them back. For to know them would be to understand the generous, passionate, vulnerable nature of literature's great master and the devotion of that master's cat.

Prologue

This is the story of my Master, Charles Dickens, the great English novelist. I tell it to you from some distant place, looking back in time to the years 1860 to 1870, the first ten years of my life and the last ten of my Master's. Where I could, I have used his words. For example, later in this Prologue I record my birth as David Copperfield recorded his. I learned the language literally at Mr. Dickens's elbow, for I was usually cuddled, front paws tucked under my chest, on his desk.

We lived at Gad's Hill Place, a lovely country house on the Dover Road, Higham-by-Rochester, Kent, England. My Master bought the house in 1856, when he was forty-four. It was for him the fulfilment of a childhood dream, but I will let him tell that story later.

Whether Dickens was in his Study or in his writing room across the road at his chalet, he was sure to have me as his companion. I belonged to him, and he belonged to me. He told me the story of his life in fragments as we sat together. I prompted them, I must admit, by a most unusual trick.

In the evening, when I grew tired of watching him read, or of seeing his pen scratch across one page of manuscript after another, I would simply stretch up on all fours, and with a quick dab of my paw extinguish the candle flame by which he read or wrote. A bemused smile would creep from the corners of his kindly eyes as he laid down his book or pen, and settled in his chair to travel back with me through the story of his life.

There is one last and most unusual thing for you to know. I relate it matter-of-factly, as most miracles are explained. I was born deaf, but I did not hold it as a disadvantage, for the simple reason that although I could not hear the songs of birds or crickets or the voice of my own dear mother, quite miraculously I could hear the voice of my Master and

1

the voices of his youngest and dearest sons, Harry and Plorn. My Master's voice was always kindly, so full of drama as he told the most wonderful stories. But to get to these stories I must first tell my own.

To begin my life with the beginning of my life, I record that I was born (as I have been informed and believe) on a Friday, at twelve o'clock at night. My mother, a most beautiful white cat named Williamina, was lying in a soft curl of blanket near the stove. Although she had a wish to be upstairs amidst the warmth and brightness of the family life, the

Williamina

Master of the house said her place was to be in the basement kitchen. So it was there that she gave birth to her little family at the midnight hour of 9 June, 1860.

My sisters and brothers and I numbered five. We were of various colours: one, all white like my mother; another, marbled brown and white; two, equal parts black and white; and one, me, a brown tabby (I prefer "tiger") with large green eyes over which, in perfect symmetry, peaked twin black lines, thus lending me a look of perpetual curiosity, which I can assure you I had.

My mother was a gentle but determined soul. She found favour with everyone in the house, but she was particularly devoted to the Master. She loved his company. For that reason, she had a fancy that her little family should live in the Study where the Master spent a good portion of his day alone, writing. So when we were still tiny kittens, she brought us upstairs, one by one, from the kitchen floor, and deposited us in a corner of the Study. We were promptly taken back downstairs by order of the Master, who said he could really not allow us to be in his room:

The Study from the hall

he was far too busy to be distracted by kittens at play. My mother tried again, with the same result. But she was not to be defeated even by a Study door, now closed fast against her. On the third trip she carried me up the stairs, but this time she continued through the hall, out through the front door, and from the geranium bed to the Study window, jumped in with me in her mouth, and laid me down at the Master's feet. She made four more trips until the whole family were at last before him. She herself sat down beside us and gave an imploring look. Kindly man that he was, he could resist no longer, and Williamina carried the day.

3

As we grew, we became very rampageous and swarmed up the curtains and played on the writing table, and scampered among the bookshelves, and made such a noise as was never heard in the Study before. We took particular pleasure in looking at ourselves in the long mirrors on either side of the bay window, and in batting the feathers of the goose quill pens as we skittered them from desk to carpet.

His desk

On that desk we also found to our delight the bronze figures of two plump toads duelling, a small monkey in a pill-box hat, a statue of a dog-fancier with dogs under his arms and puppies peering out of his pockets, a gilt leaf with a rabbit sitting erect upon it, a little box of string, a paper knife and an inkstand of blue ink. To our credit we knew enough to tiptoe among these treasures, for they were Dickens's silent companions when he wrote, there for his eyes to rest upon as he spun his plots in his head.

We pretended to read the book titles, especially those painted to look like volumes on the back of the door to the hallway. No wonder, for I later learned that one of the sets of dummy bookbacks invented and labelled by the Master bore the title *Cats' Lives* and was in nine volumes!

Our mother knew when to settle us quietly in our corner near the fireplace. The same spirit that influenced the whole house must have been

The dummy books – *Cats' Lives*

brought to bear upon us when the Master was writing, for we were never complained of, and we were never turned out of our home in the Study until the time came for finding other good homes for us.

"We will keep the little tabby," decreed the Master of the house. "He is exceptional and so must be accepted as a member of the family." He considered me singular, for in my deafness I preferred to scramble up onto his desk to keep him company while my sisters and brothers frolicked. Because I could not hear to come when summoned, I was given no name. But in consequence of my devotion to the Master of Gad's Hill, Charles Dickens, I was called The Master's Cat.

First Views of Gad's Hill Place

1

"Time to be up and doing. Come with me, Kitten. We must make our morning rounds before I start my day's writing. You must help me tend to this little country house and its large family." As he said this, Charles Dickens lifted me from his desk with his sure hand, tucked me neatly feet-first into the pocket of his grey tweed suit jacket, put his round bowler hat at a jaunty angle on his head, and we were off at a brisk pace on what was to become our morning rounds and ritual. Above us on a mast at the top of the little red brick mansion, a flag flew to proclaim that the Master of Gad's Hill Place was in residence.

Ready for the morning round

Thus I spent the first summer months of my life on this country estate investigating every nook and cranny of the house, the stables and the meadows, as my Master tended to his little Kentish freehold of twenty-six acres. He must have been the tidiest and cleverest man ever born, for nothing pleased him more than straightening and fixing. In this half hour after breakfast, he went all over the house, to the stables, and through the gardens to see that everything was just right and in order. He could not

7

bear to see a picture hanging askew, a carpet crooked, a chair out of place, or a weedy flower bed. In his other jacket pocket, balancing me, he carried a small hammer, some nails and a trowel.

Once old enough to be out of my Master's pocket and scampering on my own, it was my intention to be helpful – and, of course, amusing. I tugged stray socks from under boys' beds, found lost croquet balls under rose bushes, and chased bright butterflies among the flowers, especially the red geraniums under the front bay windows. As he inspected these, and gently scolded me out of them, my Master always picked a scarlet flower and put it through his lapel. Geraniums were Dickens's favourite flower; they suited his passion for colour. And as he also had a passion for mirrors, so did he place looking-glasses in every possible corner of the house. He chuckled when he told me one evening that his dear daughter, Katie, had laughingly told him that when he became an angel, he would wear a wreath of geraniums and have wings of bright mirror-glass. And, of course, everything around him would be very tidy.

Katie

In that summer of 1860, on our rounds we found the six children who were still at home in various places. Two of the older boys – Frank, sixteen, and Alfred, fifteen – were usually engaged in practising some outdoor sport such as football or cricket. I could only be a spectator while their father hailed their prowess, "Well run! Well run!"

Sydney – The Ocean Spectre

Sydney, at thirteen, was a dreamer but rather reckless in energy. We often found him high among the branches of a tall cedar, gazing southeast toward the river Medway and Rochester, or north to the Thames on its way to empty into the North Sea. His father had early nicknamed him the Ocean Spectre, because he had a far-away look in his eyes, as if he saw some phantom out at sea. By the end of the summer, having graduated as a naval cadet, he joined his training ship. When he came home on leave, he always coaxed me to join him up in the tree branches. The copper beech on the back lawn I could manage; but the top of a cedar tree was a bit high for my liking. I could scramble up well enough; getting down was something else.

The two younger boys – Henry, who was eleven and called Harry, and Edward, who was eight and called Plorn (short for his father's whimsical

9

invention Plornishmaroontigoonter) – were usually to be found at a game of make-believe in the shrubbery across the high road, or building some contraption out of pieces borrowed from schoolroom, kitchen or stables. These boys were my favourite companions when my Master was away in London tending to business. Harry was bright and clever, quick-witted and never idle; Plorn was shy and affectionate. They frequently needed me to be stalked in their "jungle" or to be shut up in their "castle."

Mamie, who at nineteen was amiable and high-spirited, often beat us to the stables where we would find her waiting for Marsh, the groom, to hitch the sprightly Norwegian pony Newman Noggs to the basket-phaeton or the sturdy grey cob Trotty Veck to the brougham, or simply saddle up her riding horse, Boy. Dickens greeted Marsh and, fondly teasing Mamie, said, "My daughter Mary drives anything that can be harnessed." And to bring me up to date in family history, he added, "They turned the basket-phaeton over last summer in a by-road, Mary and two friends – and had to get it up again; which they did, and came home as if nothing had happened."

Mamie

When I needed a rest from her younger brothers, I sometimes went driving with Mamie or curled up in her silk lap in the drawing-room when she sat and sewed with Georgina.

Georgina was my Master's sister-in-law, who had come to be with the children in 1842 when their parents took a trip to America. She was only fifteen then, but was so loved by the children – "Aunt Georgie," they called her – that she stayed to help raise them.

Georgina Hogarth, Aunt Georgie

Of the children no longer at home, three were grown up and gone out into the world, and one, little Dora Annie, had died when she was a baby. Charley, the eldest at twenty-three, lived in London. At his father's request he had gone to stay with his mother, Catherine, when Dickens separated from her in 1858. Walter had gone to India in 1857 at the age of sixteen as a cadet in the East India Company's 26th Native Infantry. Katie, or "Lucifer Box", as her father called her for her red-headed strong will, was twenty-one. That first summer, when I was only six weeks old, too small to be a part of celebrations, Katie was married to Charles

Collins, younger brother of one of Dickens's best friends, the author Wilkie Collins. She and her husband set up housekeeping in London, so she was not a part of our morning rounds.

Very *much* a part of our morning rounds, and at first what I took to be a very *dangerous* part, were the dogs; "a roost of dogs," the villagers called them. Inside the house there was a bossy but, I must admit, quite beguiling white Pomeranian named Mrs Bouncer. She belonged to Mamie, and as the pet of the eldest daughter felt it her duty to run the place. My Master was very fond of this little creature. As we made our rounds, he would call her with a peculiar voice he used just for her, to which she would respond at once, hurrying to him from any part of the house or garden. He delighted to see her with the large dogs, with whom she put on airs because, as my Master explained to me, "She looks so preposterously small." Well, small to him.

Mrs Bouncer

Of the large dogs there were always at least two in residence, and they were forever, it seemed, scrambling to greet my Master, whom they seemed to claim noisily as *their* master. As we rounded the corner from the garden to the stables each morning, they bounded to greet us. Glad I was those first two summer months of the security of Dickens's deep tweed pocket. From that safe haven I ventured my head out to meet nose-to-nose with Turk, a beautiful (but big) mastiff, and to blink my eyes at Linda, the soft-eyed, sweet-tempered (but large) St. Bernard.

The Sir John Falstaff Hotel

Now these dogs were, I must confess, a most valuable asset to our little freehold. Gad's Hill standing alone, with the exception of the little Falstaff Inn, and on the high road, with tramps of very low order continually passing its gates, it was necessary to protect the place by keeping dogs; and the dogs, though sweet and gentle to their owners, were rather a terror to all outsiders. Sometimes in the most dangerous and busy tramp seasons they were chained at the entrance posts to frighten off would-be intruders. In addition to their guard duty, Linda and Turk were their master's constant companions in all his long walks – and ghost-hunting escapades.

The best escapade I remember took place on an October evening in 1860. It was nine o'clock, and rumours abounded of a ghost sighted at the Higham monument. Plorn was frightened to death; Harry was not much braver, and the servants in their superstition were threatening to leave the house. Village talk and credulity were amazing. The Master decided to take prompt action. He leashed the dogs and mustered a family army. Of his older boys only Frank was at home, so he armed him and a schoolboy friend with a short stick apiece and shouldered his double-barrelled gun, well loaded with shot. Frank, who had been playing with me, gathered me up and deposited me for safety in his ample jacket pocket. What luck and what larks! I was going on the hunt!

Frank

"Now observe," Dickens warned the boys, "if anybody is playing tricks and has got a head, I'll blow it off." Immense impression. The new groom was evidently convinced that he had entered the service of a bloodthirsty demon.

The "captain" and his small band proceeded in military fashion to the monument and stopped at the gate. I peered up and out of Frank's pocket. The moon was rising, and it cast heavy threatening shadows.

The "commanding officer" summoned his courage. "Now look out! If the ghost is here and I see him, so help me, God, I'll fire at him!" Suddenly, as they entered the field, a most extraordinary, eerie noise responded – at least that is what the commanding officer called it. "A terrific noise – a human noise – and yet a superhuman noise." Frank shuddered, and I sank to the pocket bottom.

"I heard that," said Captain Dickens, and he brought his piece to his shoulder. "There it is again, portentous, derisive, dull, dismal, damnable. Forward, men," he ordered in a steady low voice. I could feel Frank advance slowly and cautiously. I dared peer over the pocket rim. Dimly I saw something huge and monstrous white come lumbering through the darkness and disappear into the thick bushes behind the monument.

"Stand firm at the ready!" the captain ordered.

Frank gripped the dogs' chains. Turk's hair bristled; Linda's rose in ripples. Sticks, dogs and shotgun were at the ready.

The bushes began to tremble. "It's coming out! Hold your fire!" ordered the captain in a hoarse whisper. And then, from the deep darkness a low hulking beast lurched into a shaft of moonlight.

What was this beast, this ghost? A bloated, ugly-looking but quite harmless asthmatic sheep!

In all humility, and gratitude, the captain and his company retreated. Upon reaching the house, the little army assumed a triumphant return, told its tale to the great relief of Plorn, Harry and the servants, and then was properly disbanded by its captain. Frank saluted me as he set me on the floor.

Gad's Hill Place – the back

★ ★ ★ ★ ★

My Master, the former commanding officer, having discharged his duties, retired to his study, there to read in peace and quiet for a few hours before bedtime. I retired with him and took my place on the table next to his armchair. I shared that table with a candle-stick whose candle

15

cast the beam by which my Master read. The light flickered across the kindly face. Dickens was forty-eight in this year 1860. Although lines of care were beginning to form at the corners of the expressive mouth and under the deep hazel eyes, his handsome oval head with its moustache and pointed beard still bore the vitality of youth. His hair, thinning and growing grey around his broad high forehead, framed his sensitive ruddy face, which he rested now on the knuckles of his long fingers as he leaned on the arm of his chair.

I allowed Dickens a half hour of this contentment. Then I silently rose, stretched my paw forward, snuffed out the candle and settled back quickly and innocently. My Master, being much interested in his book, relighted the candle, gave me a pat and went on reading. A pat was not what I had in mind. I silently rose again and extended my paw toward the flame. But this time he had me in the corner of his sharp eye, and he looked up just in time to catch me in the act.

The Master's cat

"Aha! A little fireman, are you? Putting out candle flames with your paw? Let me see that quick-as-lightning little foot," and he lifted me onto his lap for inspection. "Not singed; that's good. Is it a little attention you want?" I gazed up at him imploringly, and he understood.

"Very well; will a story do? That is what I do best, you know – tell stories. It should be one about our ghost, that harmless old asthmatic sheep. Ancient fellow was probably here when I was a boy and saw this house for the first time. Well, I do not know about him, but I do know all about that boy and how he came to be the Master of Gad's Hill.

"It all began a long time ago when I was a very small boy, not yet ten, living with my family in Chatham, not far from here. I put the true tale this way in a story I wrote for *The Uncommercial Traveller.*

"So smooth was the old high road, and so fresh were the horses, and so fast went I, in the carriage, that it was midway between Gravesend and Rochester, and the widening river was bearing the ships, white-sailed or black-smoked, out to sea, when I noticed by the wayside a very queer small boy.

"'Halloa!' said I to the very queer small boy, 'where do you live?'
"'At Chatham,' says he.
"'What do you do there?' says I.
"'I go to school,' says he.
"'I took him up in a moment, and we went on. Presently, the very queer small boy says, 'This is Gad's Hill we are coming to, where Falstaff went out to rob those travellers, and ran away.'
"'You know something about Falstaff, eh?' said I.

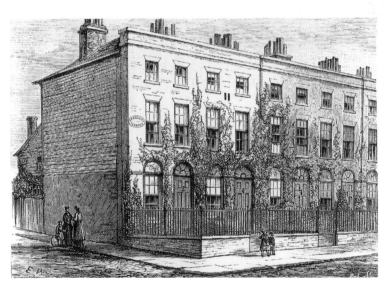

2 Ordnance Terrace, Chatham

"'All about him,' said the very queer small boy. 'I am old (I am nine), and I read all sorts of books. But *do* let us stop at the top of the hill, and look at the house there, if you please.'

"'You admire that house?' said I.

"'Bless you, sir,' said the very queer small boy. 'When I was not more than half as old as nine, it used to be a treat for me to be brought to look at it. And now I am nine, I come by myself to look at it. And ever since I can recollect, my father, seeing me so fond of it, has often said to me, "If you were to be very persevering and were to work hard, you might some day come to live in it." Though that's impossible!' said the very queer small boy, drawing a low breath, and now staring at the house out of the carriage window with all his might.

"I was rather amazed to be told this by the very queer small boy; for that house happens to be *my* house, and I have reason to believe that what he said was true.

"Indeed, the very queer small boy was I, dear Puss. I told that story about myself. I drove the carriage, and I picked up me! I was a very little and a very sickly boy. I was subject to attacks of violent spasm which disabled me from any active exertion. I was never a good little cricket player; I was never a first-rate hand at marbles, or peg-top, or prisoner's base; but I had great pleasure in watching the other boys, officers' sons for the most part (for my father was a clerk in the Navy Pay Office in Chatham), at these games, reading while they played.

The Navy Pay Office, Chatham

"My father had a small collection of books in a little room upstairs in our house to which I had access (for it adjoined my room) and which nobody else in our house ever troubled. From that blessed little room Roderick Random, Peregrine Pickle, Humphrey Clinker, Tom Jones, the Vicar of Wakefield, Don Quixote, Gil Blas and Robinson Crusoe came out, a glorious host, to keep me company. I have been Tom Jones (a child's Tom Jones, a harmless creature) for a week together. I have sustained my own idea of Roderick Random for a month at a stretch. I had a greedy relish for a few volumes of voyages and travels – I forget what now – that were on those shelves; and for days and days I can remember to have gone about my region of our house, armed with the centre-piece out of an old set of boot-trees: the perfect realization of Captain Somebody of the Royal British Navy, in danger of being beset by savages and resolved to sell his life at a great price.

"Captain Somebody! There it is, that same captain is back upon a little Kentish freehold, beset not by imaginary savages, but rather by an asthmatic sheep.

"I kept in my heart my father's words: 'If you were to be very persevering and were to work hard, you might some day come to live in it.' Well, I was very persevering, and I did work hard, and lo and behold, on my forty-third birthday, 7 February 1855, while walking from Gravesend to Rochester on a bitter day, snow piled along the way three to six feet high, I approached this mansion of dull red brick, with a little weathercock-surmounted cupola on the roof, and a bell hanging in it. And on the gate was a notice: 'For Sale.' And so in a year I had bought it – that wonderful mansion I dreamed of when I was a little boy with the first faint shadows of all my books in my head, I suppose."

2 Tombstones and Relatives

The sunshine days of my first summer at Gad's Hill gradually gave way to autumn. Fogs rolled in from the river as though to shut us up in the house. But my Master welcomed them for the air of mystery they gave to his outings.

The stable was barely visible before us as my Master made his way to it across the garden. I was glad to be bundled under his cloak against the grey drizzle. As we approached the groom, Dickens hailed him.

"Good morning, Marsh. Perfect day, isn't it?"

Although hardly in agreement, Marsh tipped his hat and smiled agreeably.

"We'll want Newman Noggs hitched up to the basket this afternoon, Marsh. No, on second thought, we'll need Trotty Veck and the brougham. A dismal drenching fog is skulking in the marshes. Just right for a visit

Marsh, Newman Noggs and carriage

to Cooling and its churchyard. Just right for Harry and Plorn to meet an escaped convict. Shiver they will, but I don't want them catching cold. Too bad that the older boys have gone off to school; they will be vexed when they hear what they have missed." Marsh again tipped his hat to Dickens, although this must have seemed to him an order for a strange ride across the countryside to the lowland carved and made sodden by the River Thames.

"We'll tell Harry and Plorn at lunch when they come in from the schoolroom, Kitten. Oh yes, you will accompany this little troop. If I am right, when you arch your back and bristle your tail, I will know I've got the scene exactly to my liking. And that is not to mention what effect it should have on the boys."

Well, now that was all a mystery; too much for me to unravel as I followed my Master to the Study for his morning's writing. Usually a carriage ride in the countryside was exactly to my liking, and I had been privileged to take a good number of them in these first months of my life at Gad's Hill. Small though I was, I never minded scampering along with the dogs on Dickens's walks, but my view of the landscape was limited to the base of hedgerows. From the seat of the brougham or the basket-phaeton, I could take in the whole picture of England's garden that was Kent: the rolling apple and cherry orchards, the hop vines twirling in the breeze on their poles, the farmyards busy with animal life and the strangely shaped oast houses. Fog or no fog, this trip promised adventure.

By three the fog had drawn a grey curtain between the stable and the meadow. The afternoon wore the mood and colour of dusk. Georgina had made sure the boys wore their hats, and she looped wool mufflers around their necks as they followed their father out of the back door to the stables.

Marsh had pony and brougham ready for the adventure. Plorn scooped me up and snuggled me between his legs on the seat as Linda and Turk took their travelling places at either side of the carriage. Dickens bounced the reins over Trotty's back, and the sturdy grey cob set off at a trot for Cooling churchyard. Three passengers were ignorant of the mission but delighted by it; the fourth was delighted by the ignorance of his companions.

On this ride I saw nothing. As we descended from the high road through the landscape of fields into the marsh country of the Thames estuary, the fog enveloped us. From inside the carriage we could only be certain there was a Trotty Veck at the end of the reins by the steady and

Cooling Church

Cooling Castle

reassuring beat of his hooves on the road. My Master knew every bend and bump by heart, for he had walked this way many times as a child and many more as a man. Nevertheless, he let Trotty have his head, trusting the pony to see into the fog where he could not.

When the ragged outline of Cooling Castle loomed close to the road on our left, my Master began to speak in a boy's voice and in time to Trotty's feet:

> My father's family name being Pirrip, and my Christian name Philip, my infant tongue could make of both names nothing longer or more explicit than Pip. So, I called myself Pip, and came to be called Pip.

Harry, Plorn and I took notice, the repeated "Pip" pinning us to the tale.

> I give Pirrip as my father's family name, on the authority of his tombstone and my sister – Mrs. Joe Gargery, who married the black-smith. As I never saw my father or my mother, and never saw any likenesses of either of them (for their days were long before the days of photographs), my first fancies regarding what they were like, were unreasonably derived from their tombstones.

Here, having secured our attention, especially riveting us with the word "tombstones," my Master pulled Trotty to a silent halt. Beckoning us with only the slightest nod, he descended from the brougham. The boys followed noiselessly. As he touched the ground, Plorn turned back to the seat, gathered me up and held me close in his folded arms. In the thick fog we bent our way, one behind the other, through the country church-yard gate. With the solemnity worthy of a funeral procession, the first figure led the smaller two between and around gravestones, until he came

The Tombstones

to a large stone set off by a line of smaller diamond-shaped ones embedded in the earth just at the corner of the little church. Pointing to the names chiselled into the stone, my Master continued in a child's voice:

> The shape of the letters on my father's, gave me an odd idea that he was a square, stout, dark man, with curly black hair. From the character and turn of the inscription, 'Also Georgiana Wife of the Above,' I drew a childish conclusion that my mother was freckled and sickly. To five little stone lozenges, each about a foot and a half long, which were arranged in a neat row beside their grave, and were sacred to the memory of five little brothers of mine – who gave up trying to get a living exceedingly early in that universal struggle – I am indebted for a belief I religiously entertained that they had all been born on their backs with their hands in their trousers-pockets, and had never taken them out in this state of existence.

As we peered down at these stone lozenges, the boys shifted their feet. Seeing that they must be tingling from the damp and from nerves, their father motioned them to sit upon the adjacent flat slab of a table tombstone. As they settled close together with their backs to the church and the cutting wind coming from the river, Plorn hugged me close. Their father resumed his tale from behind them.

> Ours was the marsh country, down by the river, within, as the river wound, twenty miles of the sea. My first most vivid and broad impression of the identity of things, seems to me to have been gained on a memorable raw afternoon towards evening. At such a time I found out for certain, that this bleak place overgrown with nettles was the church-yard; and that Philip Pirrip, late of this parish, and also Georgiana Wife of the above, were dead and buried; and that Alexander, Bartholomew, Abraham, Tobias and Roger, infant children of the aforesaid, were also dead and buried; and that the dark flat wilderness beyond the churchyard, intersected with dykes and mounds and gates, with scattered cattle feeding on it, was the marshes; and that the low leaden line beyond was the river; and that the distant savage lair from which the wind was rushing, was the sea; and that the small bundle of shivers growing afraid of it all and beginning to cry, was Pip.

Here the storyteller stopped and disappeared from us in the fog. Plorn gave me a squeeze. Even brave Harry could not check the shiver that rattled his shoulders. In the silence I could feel Plorn begin to hum ever so faintly.

'Hold your noise!' cried a terrible voice, as a man started up from among the graves at the side of the church porch. 'Keep still, you little devil or I'll cut your throat!'

My fur shot up under Plorn's clenched hands. Both boys whirled their heads around to see, to their great relief, their father, who had with a terrifying guttural voice taken on a second character in the telling of this story.

A fearful man, all in coarse grey, with a great iron on his leg. A man with no hat, and with broken shoes, and with an old rag tied round his head. A man who had been soaked in water, and smothered in mud, and lamed by stones, and cut by flints, and stung by nettles, and torn by briars; who limped and shivered, and glared and growled; and whose teeth chattered in his head as he seized me by the chin.

The fearful man

And then to face their father, the boys spun round on top of the stone to sit with their knees hugged to their chins; the master storyteller became boy and convict in frightening turns.

'Tell us your name!' said the man. 'Quick!'

'Pip, sir.'

'Once more,' said the man, staring at me. 'Give it mouth!'

'Pip. Pip, sir.'

'Show us where you live,' said the man. 'Pint out the place!'

I pointed to where our village lay, on the flat in-shore among the alder-trees and pollards, a mile or more from the church.

The man, after looking at me for a moment, turned me upside down, and emptied my pockets. There was nothing in them but a piece of bread. When the church came to itself – for he was so sudden and strong that he made it go head over heels before me, and I saw the steeple under my feet – when the church came to itself, I say, I was seated on a high tombstone, trembling, while he ate the bread ravenously.

'You young dog,' said the man, licking his lips, 'what fat cheeks you ha' got.'

I believe they were fat, though I was at that time undersized, for my years, and not strong.

'Darn me if I couldn't eat 'em,' said the man, with a threatening shake of his head, 'and if I han't half a mind to't!'

I earnestly expressed my hope that he wouldn't, and held tighter to the tombstone on which he had put me; partly, to keep myself upon it; partly, to keep myself from crying.

'Now lookee here!' said the man. 'Where's your mother?'

'There, sir!' said I.

He started, made a short run, and stopped and looked over his shoulder.

'There, sir!' I timidly explained. 'Also Georgiana. That's my mother.'

'Oh!' said he, coming back. 'And is that your father alonger your mother?'

'Yes, sir,' said I; 'him too; late of this parish.'

'Ha!' he muttered then, considering. 'Who d'ye live with – supposin' you're kindly let to live, which I han't made up my mind about?'

'My sister, sir – Mrs. Joe Gargery – wife of Joe Gargery, the blacksmith, sir.'

'Blacksmith, eh?' said he. And looked down at his leg.

By this time Harry and Plorn were blue with cold and fright. And I? My tail was standing stiff upright. My Master had acted out all this startling scene before our eyes. The fog rolling about him had shrunk him to the trembling Pip and swelled him to the threatening convict. Now in an instant with cheery voice and waving arms, he was once again our familiar Dickens.

"There it is, boys; that's the opening chapter of my new story, *Great Expectations*. Tell me, what do you think of it, my lads?"

"I think it's ripping, sir. Terribly good!" replied Harry, finding his voice and jumping down from the stone. "Does Pip bring him the file and victuals? Does he tell his sister, Mrs. Gargery, about the fearful man? Does. . ."

Here his father broke in. "All those questions have answers, Harry. I'll read the second chapter to you when I've finished it tomorrow. And what about you, Plorn? What is your considered opinion?"

"I think it's. . .it's rather scary, sir," offered Plorn, finding only half his voice and sitting tight on the stone. "I don't think Pip should ever come back here – even if it means he should never see his mother and father and brothers again."

"He won't anyway, silly boy; they're dead," teased Harry, not unkindly.

"I know that, but I just think Pip would do best to stay at home; stay with his sister and the blacksmith and not come visiting this churchyard."

"You're righter than you know, my dear Plorn," and Dickens winked at his little son. "But I'll take care of him. He has to learn some bitter lessons; but then we all do, don't we? Come, let us make our way back to Trotty so he can safely carry two boys from this churchyard."

As the father helped his sons into the brougham, he caught sight of me under Plorn's arm. He had quite forgotten me, it seems, in all this drama. But I could understand that; I had been in the family only a few months. I hoped he still wanted to know about the arch of my back and the bush of my tail.

"And how did the kitten's tail manage the tale, boys?"

Plorn was quick to reply, finding his full voice now, "Oh, he was fine, Papa. I took very good care of him, protected him from any fright, you know."

★ ★ ★ ★ ★

"So my convict gave you a fright, did he, my dear Kitten?" said my Master in a consoling voice, as he settled in his Study chair. At dinner he had delighted in the boys' version of the afternoon's adventure. So full of the tale were they that they told it to their aunt, Georgina, and sister, Mamie, by taking the parts of Pip and the convict, Plorn imitating Pip's shivering terror and Harry revelling in the fettered man's desperation. By the light of the candle next to me on the table, my Master studied the pages of his new manuscript.

"Yes, they did it justice. Capital! Capital!" And then Dickens's thoughts drifted back to the marshes, to the blacksmith's forge, to the file and the small boy who needed to snatch it and run with it back to the shrouded churchyard. Dickens worked the plot in his head, whispering it as it unfolded. How bright, how keen his eyes were – the mirrors of his mind. And then, without looking up, he spoke quietly to me.

"This boy, Pip, this orphan boy of the forge has humbler beginnings than my own. Mine were simple enough. What we had in common was what we wanted to become – gentlemen. In short, we gathered to ourselves as we grew, great expectations; and they made us ashamed of our beginnings.

"But first, let me see you do it again, Kitten. This tale of my beginnings has a dark cast. Put us in the dark."

Although permission stripped my trick of its most appealing quality – mischief – I obliged, for I was eager to know the humble beginnings of that little boy who was now the Master of Gad's Hill.

"I say dark, because my beginnings on the path to becoming the gentleman you see before you (or cannot see in this dark) were checkered, indeed. A man of property likes to think he always was. In truth, my grandparents, William and Elizabeth Dickens, were butler and housekeeper, respectively, at Crewe Hall in Cheshire. They were good, honest, hard-working folk. To my grandmother I owe a profound debt, for she was a marvellous spinner of stories. The Crewe children and her sons, William and John, gathered in her quarters to listen spellbound

John Dickens

Elizabeth Dickens

to her fairy tales and history sagas. Upon my grandfather's early death, Lord Crewe took a kindly interest in his housekeeper's sons, saw to their schooling and secured positions for them. My father, John, became a clerk in the Navy Pay Office, first in London and then; in Portsmouth.

"My mother's family claimed a higher station in life, and marriage to my mother, Elizabeth, must have seemed a step up in my father's rise into gentility. The Barrow family, however, was cast in shadow by my grandfather Charles Barrow's embezzlement of a vast sum of money from the Navy Pay Office. To make matters worse, he fled to the Continent, leaving his family in shame.

"The next generation, my father and mother, brought me unintended grief." Here my Master paused, turned and lifted me onto his lap. Moving his forefinger back and forth under my chin, he continued:

"My father was a good father, a good husband, as kind a man as ever was, but so impractical. His was a generous nature, and he simply could not live within his income. My mother was a small, pretty girl of about sixteen, with bright hazel eyes, an inordinate sense of the ludicrous, and remarkable powers of comic mimicry, cheerful, sweet-tempered and well educated. She was full of fun. I came into this world earlier than I was expected, because she could not resist going to a ball and dancing the night away. Returning to their home in Mile End Terrace, Portsmouth, in the early hours of the morning, she gave birth to me at dawn – 7 February 1812. That seemingly careless view of my life was to be the regard in which my mother held me as a small child and young boy.

"Thus, in my growing up I felt the pain of my family history, my background, and the sting of my family life, my solitude. Left to amuse myself, I pretended that I had been

Dickens's birthplace, Mile End Terrace, Portsmouth

born to great expectations, with the powers of imagination and will to acquire them.

"To be ashamed of one's beginnings and to keep them a secret is to harbour darkness. This book, Pip's story, is my penance for those false values of mine.

"Enough of both tales tonight. I will write about the little boy Pip tomorrow, and tell you about the little boy Charles another evening."

3 Warren's Blacking, 30 Strand

"Merry Christmas, the house. Where are my children? It is good to be children sometimes, and never better than at Christmas when its Mighty Founder was a child himself."

Charles Dickens, master of Gad's Hill and, for all the world, father of Christmas because of his little book *A Christmas Carol*, was standing in the front hall at the foot of the staircase, impatient to begin the festivities of the day. Oh, such a day as any child, or any grown-up, or any cat for that matter, could wish for. To my Master it was a time dearer than any other part of the year. He was always at his best, a splendid host, bright and jolly as a boy and throwing his heart and soul into everything. At his orders the house was decked with holly and mistletoe, ribbons and candles. Guests swelled our family circle until Gad's Hill was bursting with merriment. The most special guest of all was Dickens's first grandchild, Mary Angela, called Mekitty, brought to Gad's Hill by her father Charley and mother Bessie, so that her first Christmas would light the way to all others.

The morning began with a father's rousing, "I say, a merry Christmas to all the house. Be up and about this day, my children."

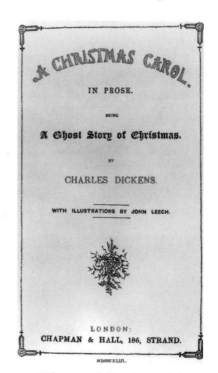

Title page of this edition of *A Christmas Carol*

31

Walter

That was the signal. Led by little Plorn, they clattered down and round the bends of the staircase, greeted their father with kisses and sturdy handshakes from the older boys, and stood expectant with him before a grand and dazzling tree in the drawing room.

> The tree was planted in the middle of a great round table, and towered high above their heads. It was brilliantly lighted by a multitude of little tapers; and everywhere sparkled and glittered with bright objects.
>
> There were rosy-cheeked dolls, hiding behind the green leaves; there were real watches (with moveable hands, at least, and an endless capacity of being wound up) dangling from innumerable twigs; there were jolly, broad-faced little men, much more agreeable in appearance than many real men – and no wonder, for their heads took off, and showed them to be full of sugar-plums; there were fiddles and drums; there were tambourines, books, work-boxes, paint-boxes, sweetmeat-boxes; there were trinkets for the elder girls, far brighter than any gold or jewels; there were baskets and pin-cushions in all devices; there were guns, swords and banners; there were witches standing in enchanted rings of pasteboard teetotums, to tell fortunes; there were humming tops, needle-cases, pen-wipers, smelling-bottles, conversation cards, bouquet holders; real fruit, made artificially dazzling with gold leaf. "There is everything and more."

The day proceeded to a great feast whose centrepiece was an enormous turkey which, like the one Scrooge gave Tiny Tim's family, "never could have stood upon his legs, that bird." And then, as he had done every year since he wrote it in 1843, my Master read a passage from Stave One of *A Christmas Carol*. Pushing back from the dinner table, he took the little volume from his coat pocket. All heads turned expectantly towards him and Harry surreptitiously lifted me onto his lap, keeping the tablecloth between me and visibility. In on the trick by the quickness of his eye, only Plorn knew I had been elevated to the party. Then came my Master's powerful low voice:

> Marley was dead: to begin with. There is no doubt whatever about that. The register of his burial was signed by the clergyman, the clerk, the undertaker, and the chief mourner. Scrooge signed it: and Scrooge's name was good upon 'Change, for anything he chose to put his hand to. Old Marley was as dead as a door-nail.

Marley's Ghost

33

With that, Plorn pulled me across his brother's knees to his own lap. An impending ghost again! Indeed, as the tale unfolded, Scrooge, that 'squeezing, wrenching, grasping, scraping, clutching, covetous old sinner', found himself meeting Marley's ghost – even though 'he locked himself in his room; doubled-locked himself in.'

> As Scrooge threw his head back in the chair, his glance happened to rest upon a bell, a disused bell, that hung in the room. It was with great astonishment, and with a strange, inexplicable dread, that as he looked, he saw this bell begin to swing. Soon it rang out loudly, and so did every bell in the house.
>
> The bells ceased as they had begun, together. They were succeeded by a clanking noise, deep down below; as if some person were dragging a heavy chain over the casks in the wine-merchant's cellar. The cellar-door flew open with a booming sound, and then he heard the noise much louder, on the floors below; then coming up the stairs; then coming straight towards his door.
>
> Then, without a pause, it came on through the heavy door, and passed into the room before his eyes. Upon its coming in, the dying flame leaped up, as though it cried, 'I know him!'

Marley's Ghost!" Plorn cried out. With the slightest smile and nod of his head, Dickens concurred:

> The same face; the very same. Marley in his pig-tail, usual waistcoat, tights, and boots. The chain he drew was clasped about his middle. It was long, and wound about him like a tail; and it was made (for Scrooge observed it closely) of cashboxes, keys, padlocks, ledgers, deeds, and heavy purses wrought in steel. His body was transparent: so that Scrooge, observing him, and looking through his waistcoat, could see the two buttons on his coat behind.
>
> 'Mercy! Dreadful apparition, why do you trouble me? Why do spirits walk the earth, and why do they come to me?'
>
> 'It is required of every man, that the spirit within him should walk abroad among his fellow-men, and travel far and wide; and if that spirit goes not forth in life, it is condemned to do so after death. It is doomed to wander through the world – oh, woe is me! – and witness what it cannot share, but might have shared on earth, and turned to happiness!'
>
> 'You are fettered, tell me why?'
>
> 'I wear the chain I forged in life,' replied the Ghost. 'I made it link by link, and yard by yard; I girded it on of my own free will, and of my own free will I wore it. Is its pattern strange to *you*? Or would you know the weight and length of the strong coil you bear

yourself? It was full as heavy and as long as this, seven Christmas Eves ago. You have laboured on it, since. It is a ponderous chain!'

Scrooge glanced about him on the floor, in the expectation of finding himself surrounded by some fifty or sixty fathoms of iron cable; but he could see nothing.

'I am here to-night to warn you that you have yet a chance and hope of escaping my fate. A chance and hope of my procuring, Ebenezer.'

'You were always a good friend to me. Thank'ee!'

'You will be haunted by Three Spirits.'

'Is that the chance and hope you mentioned, Jacob?'

'It is.'

'I – I think I'd rather not.'

"More tomorrow evening, my hearts." Plorn nudged Harry and shivered with delight. . . and relief. My Master called for steaming bowls of punch, and he led the company into the drawing room for an evening of games. Dickens loved games, especially riddles and memory challenges. One was particularly memorable this evening, because it lifted my Master back for an instant to another time and in so doing perplexed the other players.

One of the party started by giving a name, such as, for instance, Napoleon. The next person had to repeat this and add something of his

Warren's Blacking factory

35

own, such as Napoleon, Blackbeetle, and so on until the string of words began to get long and difficult to remember. My Master, after many turns, had successfully gone through the long string of words and finished up with his own contribution, "Warren's Blacking, 30 Strand." He gave this with an odd twinkle in his eye and a strange inflection in his voice, which at once forcibly arrested everyone's attention and left a vivid impression.

★ ★ ★ ★ ★

When the last game was over, and the merriment had dwindled to sleepy laughter, and the last child, little Plorn, had put his arms up to his father for a Christmas goodnight kiss, and reluctantly ascended the stairs, my Master settled in his deep chair close by the fragrant tree and glowing fire. I had only to jump onto the small table next to him, and from there onto the soft flat arm of his chair to join his reverie. No need to put out the candle; he wanted to tell me the story of another Christmas.

"A royal day, m'dear Puss. A day of joy as it should be. Ah, but I can see one a long time ago that was all misery – misery because of what was left behind and what was to come.

"It was Christmas Day 1822. I was ten, just Plorn's age, and I was on a coach bound from Chatham to London. I was a very small, very miserable ten. You see, my happy days, the days of my childhood's fancy, in this Kentish countryside were over. My father had been transferred to London and I had been left behind for two months as a lodger to finish the school term which is why I boarded the coach alone.

"Through all the years that have since passed, have I ever lost the smell of the damp straw in which I was packed – like game – and forwarded, carriage paid to the Cross Keys, Wood Street, Cheapside, London? There was no other inside passenger, and I consumed my sandwiches in solitude and dreariness, and it rained hard all the way, and I thought life sloppier than I had expected to find it.

"There followed two years of strained circumstances, for our family of seven seemed always to live beyond our father's income. My mother made plans to run a school, but no pupils came. Worst of all, I was sent again and again to pawn family possessions, even the books I so loved.

"And now I fell into a state of dire neglect, which I have never been able to look back upon without a kind of agony. To help with our family's dwindling moneys, in an evil hour for me, a relative proposed that I should go into Warren's Blacking Warehouse, to be as useful as I could, at a salary, I think, of six shillings a week. The offer was accepted very willingly by my father and mother, and on a Monday morning, two days after my twelfth birthday, I went down to the blacking warehouse to begin my business life.

"It is wonderful to me how I could have been so easily cast away at such an age. The blacking warehouse was a crazy tumble-down old house, abutting of course on the river, and literally overrun with rats. Its wainscotted rooms and its rotten floors and staircase, and the old grey rats swarming down in the cellars, and the sound of their squeaking and scuffling coming up the stairs at all times, and the dirt and decay of the place, rise up visibly before me, as if I were there again. The counting-house was on the first floor, looking over the coal-barges and the river. There was a recess in it, in which I was to sit and work. My work was to cover the pots of paste-blacking: first with a piece of oil-paper and then with a piece of blue paper; to tie them round with a string; and then to clip the paper close and neat all round. Two or three other boys were kept at similar duty downstairs on similar wages. One of them came

At work with pots of blacking

up, in a ragged apron and a paper cap, on the first Monday morning, to show me the trick of using the string and tying the knot. His name was Bob Fagin, and I took the liberty of using his name long afterwards in *Oliver Twist*.

"Bob Fagin was very good to me on the occasion of a bad attack of my old disorder. I suffered such excruciating pain in my side this time, that they made a temporary bed of straw in my recess in the counting-house, and I rolled about on the floor, and Bob filled empty blacking-bottles with hot water, and applied relays of them to my side half the day. I got better and quite easy towards evening; but Bob (who was much bigger and older than I) did not like the idea of my going home alone, and took me under his protection. I was too proud to let him know about the debtors' prison; for by now my father, having lost all of his credit, was imprisoned in the Marshalsea, there to stay until he could pay his debts. My mother, my little sister Letitia and my brothers Fred and Alfred went with him. My older sister, Fanny, was the only one spared this misery. Because of her talents she had been enrolled at the Royal Academy of

Fanny

Music as student and boarder, and there she stayed. I loved Fanny, yet it was a stake through my heart to think of my own disregarded condition. I was far away from my parents and felt abandoned. Then one Sunday, when Fanny and I were visiting the family in the Marshalsea, feeling my solitude so grievously, I broke down in front of my father. He was surprised, and moved to find lodgings for me not far from the prison. These were in the house of a fat, lame old gentleman and his quiet wife. A bed and bedding were made up for me on the floor of the back attic.

"So it was that I had no home that I could wish anyone to see. Thus, on that walk 'home' with Bob Fagin, in my pride and shame, after making several efforts to get rid of my escort, to all of which Bob Fagin in his goodness was deaf, I shook hands with him on the steps of a house near Southwark Bridge on the Surrey side, making believe that I lived there.

"No words can express the secret agony of my soul as I felt my early hopes of growing up to be a learned and distinguished man crushed in my breast. Ignorance and Want: these seemed to be the spectres of my

Ignorance and Want

39

life revealed to me. They so haunted me that they ultimately became the children in *A Christmas Carol*, clinging beneath the robe of the Spirit of Christmas Present, yellow, meagre, ragged, scowling, wolfish; but prostrate, too, in their humility. They were the message of that little story; they were the reason Marley and the Spirits haunted Scrooge. Care for them, change their lives, or mankind is doomed.

"I felt doomed, dear Puss. No advice, no counsel, no encouragement, no consolation, no support from anyone that I can call to mind, so help me God.

"I do not exaggerate the scantiness of my resources and the difficulties of my life. I know that if a shilling or so were given to me by anyone, I spent it on a dinner or a tea. I know that I worked from morning to night with common men and boys, a shabby child. I know that I tried to make my money last the week through by putting it away in a drawer I had in the counting-house, wrapped into six little parcels, each parcel containing the same amount and labelled with a different day. I know that I have lounged about the streets, insufficiently and unsatisfactorily fed. I know that, but for the mercy of God, I might easily have been, for any care that was taken of me, a little robber or a little vagabond London would have been my den.

"Where is there such a maze of streets, courts, lanes and alleys so teeming with life but in London? You should see them, dear Puss; the roofs, the chimneys, the churches, the light upon the river, and there towering above them the great cross on the summit of St. Paul's. Its huge dome loomed then through the fog and smoke over the grimy, confused city. And in the hurly-burly I saw and recorded it all: the shops for the purchase of rags, bones, old iron, and kitchen stuff. . .bird fanciers and rabbit dealers. . .dirty men, filthy women, squalid children. . .reeking pipes, bad fruit, more than doubtful oysters, attenuated cats, depressed dogs.

"Oddly enough, none of this depressed me. Quite the contrary, it exhilarated me and peopled my solitary and self-dependent state. My lifelong love of London had begun.

"That I suffered in secret, and that I suffered exquisitely, no one ever knew but I. How much I suffered it, is, as I have said already, utterly beyond my power to tell. But I kept my own counsel, and I did my work. I knew from the first, that if I could not do my work as well as any of the rest, I could not hold myself above slight and contempt.

"But I used it all. It is all there for those who read the stories of my children making their hard way in life: David Copperfield, thrown away to work in a warehouse; Little Dorrit, born in the shadow of the iron grills of the Marshalsea; Mr. Micawber's children, playing in that prison, avoiding the dark iron grill patterns cast on the gravel; Oliver Twist, trapped in the sinister, villainous, world of a pickpocket gang; or Jo, the crossing sweeper, contracting smallpox in the slums.

"And how did I escape the blacking warehouse, you ask? Owing to that business's prosperity, it moved to a new location in a well-travelled thoroughfare near Covent Garden. Bob Fagin and I had attained great dexterity in tying up the pots. (Our hands could move as fast as your little paw.) I forget how many we could do in five minutes. We were so brisk at it that we were put in the window to attract patrons, and people used to stop and look in. Sometimes there would be quite a little crowd there. One humiliation heaped upon another.

"I saw my father coming in at the door one day when we were very busy. He had been freed from the Marshalsea. He did not like the spectacle of me working for show in the window, so he withdrew me from Warren's employment. My mother, anxious about the loss of my minuscule salary, wished to send me back. My father refused to permit it. I do not speak resentfully or angrily, for I know how all these things have worked together to make me what I am; but I never afterwards forgot, I never shall forget, I never can forget that my mother was warm for my being sent back – back to Warren's Blacking, 30 Strand.

"So scalding a memory is this that I have never told it to a soul. I may some day, but until then it is disguised in my stories. Only you know it now, m'dear Puss. And we must go to sleep on it. The ghosts of my childhood have visited us, and we have kept Christmas well."

The Bat, the Bath and Boz

4

JULY 1863   GAD'S HILL GAZETTE   FIRST WEEK

THE BATTLE OF THE BAT (OR WAS IT THE BATH?)

On a recent summer night, when the heat was intense, the company – and there were several of us that evening – were seated in the hall after dinner with both doors, in front and at the back, thrown wide open; when suddenly, a bat flew into the hall and, as is the wont of bats, flew wildly high and low, backwards and forwards, causing panic among all assembled. There was a rush for protection in the rooms leading out of the hall. The bat, at last, in despair, took refuge in a recess in the ceiling which could not be reached from the floor; and there it remained – nothing would induce it to budge. Something had to be done – somebody must have the courage to do what was necessary to dislodge it. It was then that my father came to the rescue. He called for the library ladder and stick, and advanced to the attack. Suddenly it struck him that his head was uncovered, and he had misgivings lest the bat might get mixed up in his hair. No adequate protection being at hand, he called for a hip-bath – of all things! With this protection on his head, like a new kind of helmet, he put his foot upon the ladder and began to climb; but the bath being an unstable headpiece began to wobble; as he mounted, it wobbled still more and more, until the contest reduced itself into one not of between himself and the bat but between the bath and himself. It was at this critical time that the ridiculous side of the situation suddenly struck him, and he at once became convulsed with laughter, until at last the bath fell down with a crash and my father fell back on the floor quite overcome, and the attack was at an end; but luckily the bat, startled no doubt by the unusual noise below him, solved the difficulty by retreating from the hiding-place and flying out into the night.

Henry Fielding Dickens, Editor

★ ★ ★ ★ ★ ★ ★ ★ ★ ★ ★ ★ ★ ★ ★ ★ ★ ★

CRICKET MATCH
UPPER HIGHAM vs. LOWER HIGHAM
GAD'S HILL, 28 JULY

★ ★ ★ ★ ★ ★ ★ ★ ★ ★ ★ ★ ★ ★ ★ ★ ★ ★

In the summer of 1863, to keep the four youngest boys out of mischief, and that was most certainly not easy, their father encouraged them to follow in his footsteps and begin a small weekly newspaper, The Gad's Hill Gazette. Alfred, Sydney and Harry were set up in a little room fitted out as an office, complete with a bell to ring for their office-boy, Plorn.

An early number of *The Gad's Hill Gazette*

Alfred and Sydney did not stay at this enterprise long, so Harry raised Plorn to the rank of editor, and together they produced hand-written issues with a few carbon copies for family and friends. Even though Plorn, too, lost interest, Harry persevered, and a family friend rewarded his efforts by giving him a small printing press.

The Gad's Hill Gazette, by all accounts, was a lively informative newspaper reporting on our house's busy social and sporting scene: the comings and goings of guests such as Hans Christian Andersen, evening amusements, excursions, billiards and cricket matches. It told anecdotes and published puzzles and acrostics. It also ran a lively correspondence page, for which the editor's father wrote letters, assuming assorted pen-names and replying to himself as equally fictitious characters. At the peak of its circulation, the little paper had about a hundred subscribers, who paid twopence a copy, and seemed genuinely sorry to miss it during the school term, when its editor, Harry, was away at boarding school and, therefore, not available to gather the news, write the anecdotes and articles, solicit letters and set the type.

43

Alfred

Harry as a boy

I could tell Dickens was proud of Harry. On press day he often strolled into the office to watch his son print the papers. I was always glad of this trip, for I loved to tap out from under tables and cabinets any metal letters that had fallen from their cases. Harry always gave me an appreciative pat as he stooped to retrieve them from me. He was a thoughtful, industrious lad. His father could see in him the integrity and enterprise of his own youth.

★ ★ ★ ★ ★

My Master and I were in our usual place, the Study, late of an evening about a week after his battle with the bat. He was reading with great relish Harry's account of the bath balancing precariously and then toppling to the floor.

"Bless Harry; he does like a good story," chuckled Dickens, as he settled back in his chair.

Well, you will remember, I like a good story, too; so I stretched forward and snuffed out the candle. My Master lowered the Gazette and frowned through the dark in my direction.

"I suppose you want to know what became of that miserable little blacking pot labeller after he left Warren's?" prompted my Master, the feigned frown vanishing from his brow. I did. "Well, within a few years he, like Harry, was engaged in the newspaper business.

"Prior to that I was allowed to go to school for almost three years at Wellington House, where I read the classics, won prizes, and learnt to be a boy again. But this bliss was short-lived. My father put it best, when asked in later years by a friend, 'Pray, Mr. Dickens, where was your son educated?'

"'Why, indeed, sir – ha! ha! – he may be said to have educated himself.'

"Of the two kinds of education that all men receive – the first, that of his teachers, and the second, more personal and more important, his own – I had the advantage only of the last.

"When I was fifteen, our family finances once again being thin, my mother secured a position for me as office boy in a firm of solicitors. I earned the tidy sum of fifteen shillings a week; and because my love of impersonating story-book characters had grown to a devotion to theatricals in school, I dedicated a portion of my wages to theatre tickets. Soon I was taking part in amateur performances and savouring every moment before the gas lights. For the princely sum of £2 I could be Hamlet or Richard the Third for a night.

Wellington House Academy

"But I also wanted to become a reporter for a parliamentary newspaper, as that was my father's employment at that time. To do that I had to learn the dots, dashes, flies' legs and sky-rockets of shorthand. I considered that a perfect and entire command of the mystery of shorthand writing and reading was about equal in difficulty to the mastery of six

The House of Commons

languages. But I did it, dear Puss, and by the age of twenty had acquired a reputation as a top-rank reporter in the gallery of the House of Commons, not merely for accuracy in reporting but for quickness in transcript.

"It was precisely at this time that my life took a most distinct turn. Thinking a career upon the stage might just suit me, I wrote to a celebrated actor for an audition at Covent Garden. There must have been something in the letter that struck him, for a letter came back with an appointment. My sister Fanny was in the secret and was to accompany me, but I was laid up when the day came, with a terrible cold and an inflammation of the face; the beginning, by the by, of that annoyance in one ear to which I am subject to this day. I wrote to say so, and added that I would resume my application next season.

"But 'next season' was not to be. I had gained some distinction in the little world of the newspaper, which made me like it. So I began to write;

Posting his first story

didn't want money; had never thought of the stage but as a means of getting it; gradually left off turning my thoughts that way and never resumed the idea. I never told you this, did I? See how near I may have been to another sort of life.

"The angle of the turn in my life was set when stealthily one evening at twilight, with fear and trembling, I dropped my first story into a dark letter-box in a dark office up a dark court in Fleet Street. To my astonishment this little sketch of London life appeared in all the glory of print. When I purchased the magazine which held it, I turned out of the street because my eyes were so dimmed with joy and pride that they could not bear the street, and were not fit to be seen there.

"That was a memorable day for it made great changes in me. But it is the same with any life. Imagine one selected day struck out of it, and think how different its course would have been. Pause and think for a moment of the long chain of iron or gold, of thorns or flowers, that would never have bound us, but for the formation of the first link on one memorable day.

"I was twenty-one and a published writer."

5 The Fifty-Eight Boxes

My fifth Christmas at Gad's Hill held a surprise. My Master had been in London to do business with his publishers. The family and I eagerly awaited his return. We were not all that awaited him.

"The fifty-eight boxes have come, Papa," said Plorn eagerly, as he greeted his father at Higham Station.

"What?" responded Dickens. "I know nothing of fifty-eight boxes."

"Oh, Papa, really?" replied the boy. "They are piled high outside the gate, and we have all been guessing what they could possibly be." With that, Plorn lifted me onto his lap to make a place for his father.

Turk and Linda, who always accompanied the carriage for departures and home-comings, greeted their master with bouncing joy, saw him to his seat and took their places on either side of the carriage to escort him in style.

Toby, the strong carriage horse, made the harness bells jingle a two-step, as he trotted up the long hill from the station to Gad's Hill. He was as eager to get home as his master. Hearing the bells in the distance, the family and guests gathered on the front porch. The flag, raised to welcome back the Master of Gad's Hill, whipped in the brisk December air.

The carriage turned neatly in at the gate and stopped, so that the recipient of the fifty-eight boxes might have a look. With a flourish of his hand, Dickens signalled his coachman to draw up to the house, whereupon he hailed his family and guests. In a familiar and easy motion he picked me up from Plorn, snuggled me under his left arm, and descended from the carriage.

Standing at the front door, with a curious smile on his face, was one of the guests, Charles Fechter, the actor.

"Do I discern by your proprietary grin, my dear Fechter, that you are responsible for that mountain of boxes at the gate?" inquired Dickens, heartily shaking his friend's hand.

Charles Fechter

"I am; I boast I am," replied Fechter, as he bowed a deep theatrical bow.

"Well, let us not waste another minute," invited Dickens, and with me still under his arm he pivoted round and led the way down the steps to commence the unpacking himself.

The eager party carried the fifty-eight boxes onto the lawn. I bounded from one to another as they were prized and split open. Strangely carved and ornamented pieces of wood, ninety-four to be precise, emerged. Charles Fechter had brought Dickens a Swiss chalet – a real one. It was all in parts – ninety-four parts, indeed – made to fit together like the joints of a giant puzzle. My Master was elated.

Within the first month of the new year, 1865, the splendid chalet stood on its brick foundation in the Wilderness, the piece of ground belonging to Dickens across the high road. It was a place of childhood fantasies, two stories high, with an outside staircase leading to the top room, perched high among the ancient cedars.

"It is a very pretty thing, and in the summer (supposing it not blown away in the spring) the upper room will make a charming study," Dickens mused.

So we were to move! To have two studies! How exciting; nothing I liked more than to follow my Master about the house and garden. Now we would cross the high road. Such daring that would take!

The chalet

The tunnel

"No, my dear Puss, you will not cross. You can trust me to carry you back and forth. But I cannot trust you to abide patiently on the south side if I have wandered to the north without you. You will spend one too many of your bounty of nine lives on such a journey. No, I will excavate a tunnel!"

And so he did, watching with boyish delight and expectation as the workmen approached each other from opposite ends of the tunnel. As this was to be my safe passage, I was at the top of the steps on the front lawn peering with my Master down into the hole under the high road. I stretched to see, as my Master heard the sounds of picks and shovels and shouts of men rise from the deep earth. Suddenly Dickens raised his walking stick in jubilation; he heard the brick barrel-vaulted tunnel echo with cheers. The workmen had broken through and met each other. He rushed down the steps to congratulate the men. I was right behind him.

The excitement moved from the cool tunnel back up to the lawn as my Master ordered a celebration. The sturdy men, a merry band, might have been boys for all their exuberance. One among them, busily employed in brushing the dirt off his boots, straightened to address my Master in gratitude. Eventually the jolly men departed with handshakes all around, and around again.

★ ★ ★ ★ ★

When the hearty band of tunnel diggers had gone, and we had had our dinner, my Master and I stood in the Study window, gazing at the gate to the tunnel and the chalet beyond.

"Do you know what that workman said to me, dear Puss? 'Mr. Dickens, sir, it were wery kind o' you to treat my men. I never see men eat and drink so much afore. I wonder they an't afeer'd o' bustin'. As for me, I'm here to thank'ee for Mr. Pickvick and in partic'lar Sam Weller. Now there's a gen'l'm'n and 'is man. I've taken many a pleasure in their hex-traordinary and uncommon adwentures. So thank'ee, sir, thank'ee; and so long life to the Pickvicks and Wellers, says I. And to Mr. Dickens, a wery great scribbler of books.'

"You don't know Mr. Pickwick, Puss, but you saw today the kind of fun he always had – without, I quickly add, the disaster his escapades frequently incurred. Who was Pickwick, you ask? He was the delightful, rotund, bald-headed fellow with beaming eyes twinkling from behind circular spectacles, who made me famous. I wrote a book about him and his companions, their adventures and misadventures.

Mr Pickwick coming out of 48 Doughty Street

"But I am getting ahead of myself, Puss. You know so far only that at twenty-one I was published. By 1836 I had gathered together three years' worth of sketches for various monthly magazines and newspapers and published them under the title *Sketches by Boz*. That was my first book. My signature Boz was the nickname of a pet child, a younger brother, whom I had dubbed Moses, in honour of the Vicar of Wakefield; which, being humorously pronounced through the nose, became Boses and, being shortened, became Boz. Boz was a familiar household word to me, long before I was an author, and so I came to adopt it.

"No sooner was my first book out than I began on my second. That was *The Pickwick Papers*. Now I had a steady income, and I could turn my thoughts to matters of the heart.

"For a time when I was just seventeen, I was desperately in love with a young woman named Maria Beadnell, but she only toyed with my affection and left me miserable. When I was twenty-three, I met Catherine Hogarth, daughter of my editor at the *Evening Chronicle*. I was very

53

His youngest brother, Augustus (Boz)

much taken with her, dear Puss; I even moved my lodgings in order to be near the Hogarth home. A year later, April 1836, we were married.

"And thus began my family – both families; the family that bears my name and the family I have created with my pen. I know my own children think that the children of my brain are much more real to me at times than they are. Charley and the others have heard me often and

Maria Beadnell

Catherine

often complain that I *cannot* get the people of my imagination to do what I want, and that they will insist on working out their histories in *their* own way and not *mine*. You see, these children of my pen – Oliver, Nicholas, Nell, David, Pip, Florence, Tiny Tim, Sissy and Little Dorrit, all of them – flock round my table in my quiet writing hours, each one of the host claiming and demanding instant personal attention.

"Oh, me. Well, perhaps now with the chalet, I can keep that host across the high road. We'll make the tunnel out of bounds. That's it, Puss. The tunnel will be for you and me. Not even Mr. Pickwick will be allowed to venture there."

Brightness of Fire and Fame

6

He cut a handsome figure, my Master did, as he stood at the top of the steps leading out of the house to the back garden and the meadow beyond. For a man in his fifties, who had led such a driving life, he was animated, erect, and dapper. He was dressed for the summer day in his cricket whites, for he was host to the Higham Eleven in its annual Gad's Hill match against another village's team. In his characteristic stance, head thrown back, hat cocked to one side, left hand in his trousers pocket, he stood for several moments surveying the cricket pitch in the meadow. All had to be just right, umpire's marquee set up, chairs arranged, flags flying. This was serious business, this fun.

The village folk streamed down the lane next to the stables and across the meadow to the field. They were eager for this day; besides a rousing match, plenty of hearty food and cooling drinks – the favourite, Aunt Georgie's cyder cup, there was the company of their famous neighbour and host, Charles Dickens.

Admonishing me to view the affair from a safe spot on top of the garden wall, my Master passed through the wrought-iron gate with GHP, for Gad's Hill Place, scrolled through its pretty pattern. He waved back at me, I think to be sure I was obeying, for he did not wish me to be lost in the crowd, and then went about greeting his guests.

Cricket at Gad's Hill. Charles Dickens bowls the first ball

Dickens himself officiated as scorer, and wore his double glasses so as to perform this, his favourite duty, just right. He conscientiously presided over the afternoon, scoring down "byes" and "overs" and "runs", and cheering even undistinguished hits with "Well run! Well run!" just as he always did his sons. His vivacity never flagged, nor his geniality as a host.

At the end of the match a Sergeant of the Guard walked up to the Master of Gad's Hill, and words passed between them. Quite amused and still blushing, Dickens related these words to me as he lifted me from the wall on his return to the house.

"A jolly fellow, that Sergeant. He asked, 'May I look at you, Sir?'

"'Oh, yes!' says I quickly, not knowing quite what to say.

"The Sergeant stared earnestly at me for a minute or so, then stood at attention, gave a military salute and said, 'God bless you, Sir!'" My Master added quietly, shaking his head, "Such is my fame, dear Puss. Such is my fame."

Dickens paused on the top step and turned to gaze at the emptying meadow.

"All in all, a good day. Yes, it was well done. Now we must conclude it with a great bonfire, for this fame of mine gives me pause. I wish to be remembered only by my books. After supper we will return to the meadow – yes, you may come this time – and we will burn all my correspondence. Oh, such a blaze it will make. I must tell Harry and Plorn and ask Georgina to get the onions ready for roasting." And with this determined, my Master carried me into the house.

Mamie and Georgina were not in favour of this conflagration and refused to assist. Katie, home for a visit, assented, however reluctantly. Harry and Plorn thought it even better sport than the day's cricket. So after supper, in the dusk of the September evening, the famous writer, his daughter and his two youngest sons carried heavy baskets full of letters

The Master reading to Mamie and Katie

to a roaring fire in the back field. They fed the flames several thousand pieces of correspondence. The boys and I fairly danced round the roaring blaze, scurrying when the wind shifted and sent smoke and flames licking at us, smarting our eyes. Katie implored her father again and again to save this letter or that, holding it out to him beseechingly. But to no avail; my Master would not be deterred.

"We should always remember that letters are but ephemeral," he declared over the crackling blaze. "We must not be affected too much either by those which praise us or by others written in the heat of the moment." Then when he, himself, had pitched the last neatly tied bundle of letters into the flames, he turned to Harry and Plorn. "Now, boys, run and get the onions from your Aunt Georgie. We'll let the fire die of its

Edward (Plorn)

own miserable indigestion, and in its ashes we'll roast the onions for ours."

As the boys raced one another to the house, disappearing from us in the dark, Dickens turned his face to the starving flames. It was a weary face, deep-lined now and devoid of the morning's vivacious air. With a deep sigh he said, "Would to God every letter I have ever written was on that pile."

A little before twelve o'clock, with the night air full of the smell of smoke and roasting onions, my Master left Katie in charge of the boys and wended his way toward the house. I did not have to run to keep up, for Dickens walked very pensively and slowly, his left leg obviously paining him now.

★ ★ ★ ★ ★

Once in the study my Master lit the candle, set it on his desk in the bay window, and invited me with a pat of his hand to settle next to his writing paper. He was about to make amends for burning all that correspondence by writing still another letter! As he dipped his pen into the ink-well, heavy rain began to pound the gravel driveway – silently for me, thunderously through the open windows for my Master. Then the heavens opened, and it poured. His pen saluted an old friend to whom he wrote:

Charles Dickens writes a letter

"Yesterday, I burnt, in the field at Gad's Hill, the accumulated letters and papers of twenty years. They sent up a smoke like the Genie when he got out of the casket on the sea-shore; and as it was an exquisite day when I began, and rained very heavily when I finished, I suspect my correspondence of having overcast the face of the Heavens."

The letter completed, Dickens put his pen in its tray, sat back against the curve of his chair, joined his hands behind his head and invited me to put out the candle flame.

"In the darkness let me tell you, about the brightness of happier days when all those letters were written, and when I attained to the fame saluted today by that Sergeant."

I snuffed out the candle with a quick jab of my paw and settled back down on the table, facing the same direction as my Master, looking out into the clean cool night.

"My success began with Pickwick, remember. Pickwick plucked strings in readers' hearts, and more and more hearts as number succeeded number. Whitehall and Whitechapel, Belgravia and Bermondsey, St George's Hanover Square and St George's in the Borough alike awaited their

48 Doughty Street

appearance. And all those shillings paid the rent for my new home, my first house, 48 Doughty Street, Mecklenburgh Square. I moved in with Catherine, with Charley (still under three months old), and with Charley's nurse. My brother Fred lived with us. Catherine's sister, Mary, spent as much time under our roof as she did under her parents'. Life was good. As if to emphasise how precious it was, a cruel blow deprived Mary of hers. I mourn her still. Yet life went on, and was still good.

"We were nearly three years at Doughty Street. *Pickwick* was finished there, and most of *Oliver Twist* written. As editor, I published parts of it each week in *Bentley's Miscellany*. *Nicholas Nickleby* was begun and completed at Doughty Street. I even wrote a little of *Barnaby Rudge* there. I wrote short stories and a play. I edited the memoires of Grimaldi, the clown. I was more busy than ever I dreamed I could be. Yet there was time too for the theatre, parties, dinners, holidays. Life was busy, life was full.

"And so a patten was established. I wrote in parts, monthly or weekly, and listened to what readers were saying. It is like being an actor watching the audience. You know when they are hanging on your words and when they aren't. You know what you must do to win them. And win them I did. Readers lined the docks in Boston, New York and Philadelphia as the ships from England came within hailing distance, bearing the latest parts of *The Old Curiosity Shop*. "Is Little Nell dead?" 'Does Nell die?'

"After monthly or weekly serialisation I put these stories in book form, and so they found their way onto bookshelves next to those great authors I had revered in my youth: Henry Fielding, Oliver Goldsmith and the rest. I was not so stunned by the praise which sounded in my ears, notwithstanding that I was keenly alive to it – a man who has any good reason to believe in himself never flourishes himself before the faces of other people – I retained my modesty in very self-respect.

Charles Dickens in Doughty Street

Catherine Dickens in Doughty Street

Charley, the eldest son

"Ah, but I dressed for the splendid part into which this fame had catapulted me. In my twenties I arrayed my sprightly trim figure in a swallow-tail coat with a high velvet collar and ballooning stock with a double-breasted pin. To outshine the gold of that pin, a heavy watch chain hung in two graceful loops from pocket to pocket of my crimson velvet waistcoat. In my thirties and forties I was no less brightly arrayed. At an evening affair I might be seen in a brass-buttoned dress coat with a red silk lining, a vest of black satin with white satin collar and a richly embroidered shirt. I must admit that among my circle of friends I called myself 'the Inimitable.' What a circle that was – the greatest novelists, poets, actors, artists and illustrators of the day. Why, I named my children after those friends.

"I matched the brightness of my clothes and of that circle of friends with a quick, keen, restless energy. My only comfort was in Motion. To clear my brain, to fill it with pictures of people and scenes of life, I walked; twelve miles a day was nothing to me. I had to see the world to know it; so I travelled abroad to America, France, Italy, Switzerland. Not easy, dear Puss. In 1846 it took three carriages and five days to get

Dickens the dandy

63

the whole family to Paris. But I had to see it all for myself. I wandered into hospitals, prisons, palaces and wine shops. I took in the panoramas of gaudy and ghastly sights. Always moving, always busy, I was a top in full spin. And my pen kept pace with me.

"After *Pickwick*, stories rolled sometimes two at once from those goose quills of mine. For twenty years, from 1838 to 1858, I conjured up close to two thousand intriguing characters: some heroes, some villains, all distinct and entertaining. I have told you that often, try as I might, I could not get these creatures of my brain to do what I wanted. Once jotted down in my little green-covered notebook, they took possession of me, went about the business of their lives, badgered me with their pasts, pointed me to their futures. I listened to them and responded by writing their stories as fast as I could. So Oliver Twist was learning to pick pockets with Fagin's gang at the same time as Nicholas Nickleby was saving Smike from a beating by the wicked one-eyed Squeers. When Scrooge and Tiny Tim tugged at my sleeve in October 1843, I had to leave Martin Chuzzlewit stranded in America in order to save that old miser and crippled boy by Christmas. No sooner had Sissy Jupe succeeded in redeeming the fact-loving Gradgrind of *Hard Times* than Little Dorrit took up her childhood days in the Marshalsea debtors' prison.

The Dream

"In profusion these characters inhabited my London Study, until I had written *Oliver Twist* and *Nicholas Nickleby, The Old Curiosity Shop, Barnaby Rudge, Martin Chuzzlewit, A Christmas Carol, Dombey and Son, David Copperfield, Bleak House, Hard Times, Little Dorrit* and *A Tale of Two Cities.* And that is not even to mention my ghost, goblin, fairy and love stories for my magazines, *Household Words* and later *All the Year Round.* And then there are the characters who have surrounded me here at Gad's Hill. You have watched me write their stories: *Great Expectations* and *Our Mutual Friend.*

"Yes, *Pickwick* made me celebrated in my youth; the rest have made me famous in my time. The host will, I trust, carry my fame into the future. If, that is, people will read me.

"Now, just for fun, I will light the candle. Let me see you put it out." My Master struck the match and touched it to the wick. I rose to my feet, turned to face the man I had come to esteem as well as love, and gave him a salute that returned the room to darkness.

7 The Frozen Deep

Although never predictable, my adventures at Gad's Hill were determined as much by the forces of nature as by the habits (or whims) of my Master. So it was that in the winter of 1865 the hurly-burly of a gigantic blizzard held us in its clutches. Snow fell in a great, velvet, white curtain, enfolding our little red brick house, its sleeping gardens and deserted roadways in deep rolling mounds. Blinking out of the billiard room window in the direction of the place the meadow should be, I marvelled at this vast new world. The boys marvelled, too, but in delight rather than awe. This was the winter weather Harry and Plorn had been waiting for. They could build forts in the meadow and amass arsenals of solidly packed snowballs, missiles to hurl on signal at one another over crenellated parapets.

My Master, like his sons, took boyish delight in the glistening alabaster world. Nothing invigorated him more than tramping out in it in his high boots, great quilted overcoat and broad-brimmed felt hat. Linda and Turk as usual would be his guides, his sled dogs without the sled, breaking a path for him through the snow.

Appearing suddenly behind me and lifting me from the window seat so that we might blink out at the whiteness head by head, he cajoled, "You don't feel disposed, do you, to muffle yourself up and start off again with me for a good brisk walk?"

I would need more than a muffler; it would be a deep pocket for me, and though I might be considered a nuisance or a burden by most men, my Master, whose left leg and foot pained him regularly now, strode out as though the weight of my small frame lodged on his right hip were nothing to him.

It was the stride of a great actor, however, for I had watched perplexed these past several snowy days as he pulled his boot over his swollen foot.

A playbill – *The Frozen Deep*

Our tramps out were long, and his feet got wet through. His boots hardened and softened, and still each day he forced the boot on. Worst of all, he sat in it to write half the day; walked in it through the snow the other half; forced the boot on the next morning; sat and walked again; and, being accustomed to all sorts of changes in his feet, took no heed. He thought it only a case of frost-bite, and so dismissed it and endured the pain.

As we approached the stables to collect the dogs, Linda was first to bound out, plunging through the snow, chest-high on her thick coat. She was in her element, for she had come as a puppy straight to Gad's Hill from the St. Bernard monastery in the Alps. Though having no such glorious heritage, Turk pitched through the snow, diving this way and that, gobbling great mouthfuls, which peaked rather than slaked his curiosity, as it mysteriously melted on his tongue.

Deciding it was foolhardy to launch out across the meadow and thus put ourselves in the line of fire of the snowballing boy-artillerymen, we took the lane by the stables skirting the battleground. We were off to our neighbour Lord Darnley's estate, Cobham Hall. Though quite a distance, especially in the deep snow, it was shorter than most of my Master's daily walks, and I suspected he had chosen it because of his foot. It was, however, one of his favourite walks.

Cobham Hall

The boughs of the stately trees of Cobham Wood hung heavy with snow. Hares, rabbits, partridges and pheasants scudded and plunged like mad across and across the chequered ground before us. Turk and Linda, obedient to their master's command, held back from giving chase to the plentiful game, though Turk's breath puffed his great jowls in and out in rapid motion.

We spent an exhilarating hour tramping through the park; the old Hall, solemn and grand, seemed to stand sentinel. And then we set out on the hour's journey home. I could feel Dickens's stride fall into the unsteady rhythm of short, light step onto left foot; quick, heavy step onto right. The good leg was pulling the bad. For this reason, my Master chose to direct our way to the village of Cobham; we could walk along the road back to Gad's Hill rather than forge our way through the deep fields. At the pub called The Leather Bottle, he paused for a moment, thinking he

The Leather Bottle, Cobham, Kent

might go in to rest his throbbing foot. Deciding that Linda and Turk were too large and too wet to be welcome guests, he turned down the road, cheering his companions on with, "Mr. Pickwick takes his pleasure here, but we will trudge on to the comfort and warmth of home."

We had travelled halfway to Gad's Hill, passing no one, for no one, was out, when to our horror our Master fell. He stumbled lame to the ground, managing to roll on his sore leg, so I would not be caught beneath him in his right pocket. I sprang out onto the broken snow crust and butted my way in between Turk and Linda, who had wheeled in their tracks and rushed to their master. There we stood, dumb-struck, not knowing how to comfort him, how to help him up, how to get him home. It was he who always took care of us; and in our fright, it was he who did so now. As he lifted himself onto his hands and good knee, he rallied us in his gentle voice.

"A bad business, this foot of mine, and embarrassing, too. Forgive me, friends; it was just an awkward stumble. Do not fret yourselves." As he made a move to shift his weight, so he could stand on his right leg, a sharp pain must have shot through his left, for he grimaced. Realizing our terror, and being struck with a solution to his dilemma, he instantly transformed his spontaneous cry of pain into a forced chuckle.

"Ah! Oh, ho, ho, ho; Linda, come. Turn round, old girl. I will lift myself by holding onto your great neck and back. At last you may claim a rescue in the snow worthy of your ancestors in the Alps." With that our master grasped Linda's massive frame and pulled himself to his feet. Turk looked on in sympathy and fear, biting at the air and pounding the snow with his front paws. Linda stood stolidly, but I could tell she was wholly struck down. Even her master's praise did not console her.

"Well done! That's a fine girl. Come on now, only three miles and we'll spot the little weathercock on top of the cupola." As he bent to lift me to his pocket, my Master winked at me. "I would bet a gold coin, you'll not accept another invitation to walk with me; not in mid-winter anyway."

Our journey home was very slow. Dickens limped heavily. Both dogs crept next to him, one on either side, all the way. Finally, late in the afternoon, turning from the lane onto the high road, and then through the front gate, our weary band rejoiced to be home. My Master stopped, and, resting a hand on each dog's head, said warmly, "You are beasts of distinctive intelligence and temperament. Let no man question or doubt it."

It was Plorn who spotted us from an upstairs window. The exhausted artillerymen had been posted by their Aunt Georgie as sentinels, one at

Georgie reading to Mamie

a front window, one at a back. Plorn sent the alert through the house and, to his pleasure, beat his brother to the porch. Behind them appeared Georgina and Mamie. At their father's insistence the boys took the dogs into the house and downstairs to the kitchen, there to be fed and thoroughly dried before retiring to the stables.

★ ★ ★ ★ ★

For the next few days Dickens was "laid up," as he called it, on the sofa in the drawing room. So it was there that I kept him company. He was not good at being laid up, nor did it seem to rest him. By the third evening, he was fitful. The candle's light revealed a hectic flush on his face. His hair was thinner and greyer, and there was a deeper earnestness in his eyes than his fifty-three years warranted. It was time for more story, so I reached for the candle. He caught sight of my advancing paw.

"A capital idea, Puss. Yes, put it out. I have just been thinking back to another frightful walk I made eight years ago. It was not in the snow, but in the dark. So let us be in the dark for the telling.

"You know well that I am a driving man; perhaps I am a driven man. When I was a child, I was driven by the threatening poverty of my family. When I became a successful writer, I was driven by that very success. There always seemed something lacking in my life, something I could not quite attain. And, also, I have always been plagued by one infirmity or another – none of which I would admit. You remember I was a sickly boy in Chatham and then given to attacks of spasms in the blacking factory. When I was thirty-three, I had a bad fall in Italy. After a tramp in the countryside, I was hurrying to get back into Genoa before the gates closed. In the dark I did not see a pole across the road, and I tumbled over it, injuring my kidneys, I fear. Well, for all of my brisk step and jaunty air, I have been plagued with botheration of one sort or another forever, it seems: growling colds, rascally rheumatism, swollen left arm and hand, this swollen foot, and – blow to my vanity – swollen face upon occasion.

"But I also have will power. Too late to say 'put the curb on and don't rush the hills.' I have now no relief but in action. I am become incapable of rest. I am quite confident I should rust, break and die if I spared myself.

"My greatest regret, dear Friend, is that I have not spared those close to me. In May of 1858, after twenty-two years of marriage, Catherine and I separated. I settled her in a London house, and I moved the children with me here to Gad's Hill. Charley, obeying my wishes, stayed with his

Catherine Dickens

Charley

mother. Such a separation caused a terrible stir; but our temperaments were not suited to one another. We had grown apart. The giggling, girlish twenty-one-year-old I had married, the fresh-coloured and elegantly gowned twenty-eight-year-old I took to America became in her thirties withdrawn, even as I became more social. By the time we were in our forties, we lived in vastly different worlds. Mine was quick-paced; I was a celebrated writer, editor, actor, public reader of my works. Catherine's was slow-paced; she was home-bound, surrounded by nine children and countless servants, and she preferred it that way.

"Now, Puss, here is the rub. You will note I referred to myself as an actor. Harking back to my old love of the theatre, I joined my friends in amateur productions. It was in one of these, "The Frozen Deep," that I acted with Mrs. Ternan and two of her daughters. The youngest, Ellen, without intention on her part and in all innocence, found her way into my heart. I, too, was innocent, for I idealized her, imagined her a princess in a castle. I sought her company, but with honourable intentions. This friendship only further distressed my life with Catherine.

The cast of *The Frozen Deep*

"The walk in the dark, the memory of which worked this sad tale out of me occurred in October of 1857, seven months before our separation. Catherine's mother and father were staying with us in Tavistock House in London. One evening some disagreement flared. I was very much put out and unable to sleep after retiring. By two in the morning, feeling it would be better to be up and doing something rather than lying in bed, I rose, dressed and set out on a walk. I had bought Gad's Hill a year and a half before, and we had spent the summer months there. Instinctively my feet turned towards this little estate, towards Kent, towards home. It was a distance of some thirty miles. The road was so lonely in the night that I fell asleep to the monotonous sound of my own feet, doing their regular four miles an hour. Mile after mile I walked, without the slightest sense of exertion, dozing heavily and dreaming constantly. I babbled a foreign language, created verses, imagined a princess in a fairy tale castle. Seven hours of this, dear Puss; not in snow but in a frozen deep.

"Now that is my dark tale. I will light the candle, so that I may make my way to bed."

8 A Railway Accident

On the 9th of June (a fateful day to him, as you will see), 1865, my Master was in the terrible railway accident at Staplehurst. He was not injured, but his nerves were shattered. He allowed himself no time to recover. He kept busy writing his seventeenth book, *Our Mutual Friend*; and in the evenings when I thought the strain on his face seemed to grow too great, I would stretch out my paw and extinguish the candle so he might have some peace. The consolation he found in my company and in the darkness of the Study contrived, oddly enough, one evening to draw the dreadful story from him. He lifted me from the table onto his lap, and as he gently stroked me, he recreated the scene.

"I was in the first carriage that did not go over into the stream. It was caught upon the turn by some of the ruin of the bridge and hung suspended and balanced in an apparently impossible manner. Two ladies were my fellow passengers, an old one and a young one. This is exactly what passed. You may judge from it the precise length of the suspense:

"Suddenly we were off the rail and beating the ground as the car of a half-emptied balloon might. The old lady cried out, 'My God!' and the young one screamed. I caught hold of them both (the old lady sat opposite and the young one on my left), and said: 'We can't help ourselves, but we can be quiet and composed. Pray don't cry out.' The old lady immediately answered: 'Thank you. Rely upon me. Upon my soul I will be quiet.' We were then all tilted down together in a corner of the carriage, and stopped. I said to them thereupon: 'You may be sure nothing worse can happen; our danger must be over. Will you remain here without stirring while I get out of the window?' They both answered quite collectedly, 'Yes,' and I got out without the least notion of what had happened.

The Staplehurst railway accident

"Fortunately I got out with great caution and stood upon the step. Looking down I saw the bridge gone and nothing below me but the line of rail. Some people in the two other compartments were madly trying to plunge out of the window and had no idea that there was an open swampy field fifteen feet below them, and nothing else.

"The two guards (one with his face cut) were running up and down on the down side of the bridge (which was not torn up) quite wildly. I called out to them: 'Look at me. Do stop an instant and look at me, and tell me whether you don't know me.' One of them answered: 'We know you very well, Mr. Dickens.' 'Then,' I said, 'my good fellow, for God's sake give me your key and send one of those labourers here, and I'll empty this carriage.' We did it quite safely, by means of a plank or two; and when it was done, I saw all the rest of the train, except the two baggage vans, down in the stream. I got into the carriage again for my brandy-flask, took off my travelling hat for a basin, climbed down the brickwork, and filled my hat with water.

"Suddenly I came upon a staggering man covered with blood (I think he must have been flung clean out of his carriage), with such a fright-ful cut across the skull that I couldn't bear to look at him. I poured some water over his face and gave him some to drink, then gave him some brandy and laid him down on the grass; and he said, 'I am gone,' and died afterwards. Then I stumbled over a lady lying on her back against a little pollard-tree, with the blood streaming over her face (which was lead colour) in a number of distinct little streams from the head. I asked her if she could swallow a little brandy, and she just nodded, and I gave her some and left her for somebody else. The next time I passed her, she was dead. Then a man came running up to me and implored me to help him find his wife, who was afterwards found dead.

Helping the wounded

"No imagination can conceive the ruin of the carriages or the extraordinary weights under which people were lying, or the complications into which they were twisted up among iron and wood, and mud and water.

"As I moved about on my errands of mercy among the dead, the dying and the wounded, I thought I heard faint groans coming from one of the carriages. I caught hold of one of the labourers, but he could hear nothing. However, upon my insisting that I heard groans, and that someone was buried under the ruins, we both set to work and in a few minutes extracted a young man whom we found jammed among the ruins upside down. He was bleeding at the eyes, ears, nose and mouth. In the moment of going over the viaduct, the whole of his pockets were shaken empty. He had no watch, no chain, no money, no pocket book, no handkerchief when we got him out. He had been choking a quarter of an hour when I heard him groaning. If I had not had the brandy to give him at the moment, I think he would have been done for.

"As I prepared to quit this scene of death, my usefulness spent and my duty done, I remembered that this manuscript, *Our Mutual Friend* (here on the desk before me), was still in the pocket of my overcoat in the dangling carriage. Not in the least flustered at the time, I climbed back into the carriage and retrieved it.

"The horror of all this is unimaginable, dear Puss. To this hour I have sudden vague rushes of terror, which are perfectly unreasonable, but quite insurmountable. I told the landlord of the Falstaff Inn down the road that I never thought I should be here again. And when Charley came this week to see me, I know he found me greatly shaken, for as he drove me in the basket-carriage, I was obliged to ask him repeatedly to make the Norwegian pony, Newman Noggs, go slower until we came to foot pace, and it was still, 'Go slower, Charley.'"

As he finished his story, my Master stopped stroking me and began to twist round and round the gold ring he wore on his little finger. "I am most thankful that my companions, Ellen Ternan and her mother, were spared. I should be at a loss had disaster befallen them. Once before I beheld the life go from a beautiful young woman. This was her ring, Puss. I gave it to her when she came to live with my wife, her sister Catherine, and me in our house in London. You see, when Charley was born, Catherine needed Mary to help her. From the day of our marriage,

Ellen Ternan   Mary Hogarth

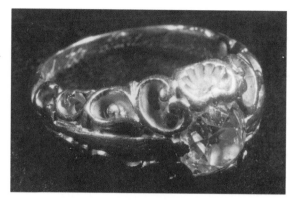

Mary's ring

the dear girl had been the grace and life of our home, our constant companion and the sharer of our little pleasures. She was seventeen, still a child in whom I at twenty-five, burdened with the duty of supporting not only Catherine and Charley but my own mother and father and brothers, could still see the glad world of childhood. She became another

Charles Dickens wearing Mary's ring

sister to me like the Fanny I had known in Chatham. I can recall everything we said and did in those happy days. She had not a single fault but, alas, a weak heart unbeknownst to those who loved her.

"It was an evening in May; Catherine, Mary and I had just returned to our home in Doughty Street from seeing a performance of a play. Saying good-night, Mary parted from us at midnight and went to her room. To our great alarm we heard her give a cry. Rushing upstairs, we found her collapsed. The doctor was called, but she never recovered. At three o'clock the following afternoon, she died in my arms. It was then that I took this ring from her finger and put it on mine. If only it could banish the emptiness I felt at the loss of one whose society had been for a long time the chief solace of my labours.

"The terrible pain in my side which had crippled me in the blacking factory returned. I could not continue to write and missed a monthly instalment of *Pickwick* and *Oliver Twist*. And when I resumed writing, Mary became Rose Maylie of *Oliver Twist* and later Little Nell of *The Old Curiosity Shop*, and Florence of *Dombey and Son*, and all the gentle, innocent and virtuous heroines of my stories. On her tombstone I had engraved 'young, beautiful and good.' Ellen Ternan is like Mary in that.

"Oh, Puss, we have learned from sad experience the uncertainty of life. I am deeply grateful for those spared that terrible train calamity."

9 The Lessons of Animals

The summer of 1865 was not to pass without another frightful encounter with a train. This one would take from us our beloved gentle giant, Turk.

That great mastiff was my Master's favourite. Companion with Linda in all of Dickens's walks, he would act as protector, explorer and guide. Usually the two dogs trotted on either side of the dapper country squire as he strode down the middle of a lane, once in a while tapping the ground with his blackthorn stick. Sometimes catching the scent of a rabbit or a hedgehog, Turk would bound ahead or off at a slant into a meadow or wood. Linda, ears cocked in curiosity, would lift her enormous feet and gallop after her partner. Usually Dickens would call them back, but sometimes they could get in a long run while their master was lost in thought. Always they circled back to him and fell into his four-mile-an-hour pace.

Always except for once. That once, in his preoccupation with the chase, Turk dashed across the tracks in front of an oncoming train. He was hit and killed instantly. Linda was just far enough behind him to be able to break her headlong plunge and stop short of the speeding train, her skidding stiff front legs absorbing the momentum of her great body.

The remorse, the sorrow, that filled the hearts of our little family at Gad's Hill knew no bounds. Plorn and his father were disconsolate. Try as I might, for days I could bring them no cheer. The boy would wander the property, scuffing the gravel of the driveway or snapping off twigs of bushes. The father would sit in the silence of the evening, pen in hand but no words coming from it.

Without her companion, Linda was listless. She padded back and forth on the stable floor or lay in the doorway waiting for Dickens. They took their afternoon walks as before; and although their pace was the same, their heart for the excursion was not.

Turk with his master

Thus the summer days dwindled down and September's brilliant skies arrived to cheer us. It was while my Master was in London for a few days that something else arrived to cheer us. An old friend made Dickens a gift of an Irish bloodhound named Sultan. Everyone thought him splendid, for he was built and coloured like a lioness. I thought him terribly large and quite as fierce as a lioness, for he had the walk, the great stride, of a wild beast. Sadly, he proved to bear out my fears.

When Dickens arrived home, he was very pleased to find Sultan. He wrote to the giver, "I cannot thank you too much for Sultan. He is a noble fellow, has fallen into the ways of the family with a grace and a dignity that denote the gentleman and came down to the railway to welcome me home (it was our first meeting), with a profound absence of interest in my individual opinion of him which captivated me completely. I shall take him about the country to improve his acquaintance. (He has only swallowed Bouncer once, and temporarily.)"

Sultan was immediately fond of his new master and was gentle and obedient with him. He was affectionate with the family and romped with Plorn. But there his good nature ended. I did not venture out of the Study and Mrs Bouncer stayed in Mamie's bedroom, for Sultan was so ferocious with everyone else that he had to be kept muzzled. He was not fitted for the sort of life he led, and the chaining up in the yard made him even fiercer than he was naturally. Dickens had a wish that he should sleep in the hall at night, and this was tried. But Sultan didn't like it and wanted to be with Linda at the stable. Finding that barking had no effect in getting his release, he set to work to bite his way out if possible. By the morning he had bitten a large piece out of the front door.

As if that weren't warning enough, he exercised certain strong dislikes – for neighbours' dogs, for strangers, for policemen, for soldiers. In December Dickens wrote to the giver, "Sultan has grown immensely, and is a sight. But he is so accursedly fierce towards other dogs, that I am obliged to take him out muzzled. Also he has an invincible repugnance to soldiers, which in a military country is inconvenient. Such is the spirit of the dog that, with his muzzle tight on, he dashed into the heart of a company in heavy marching order (only the other day) and pulled down an objectionable private. Except under such provocations, he is as gentle and docile with me as a dog can possibly be.

"Last night the gardener fired at some man in the garden, upon whom he came suddenly, and who attacked him in a desperate manner. I immediately turned out, unloosed Sultan and hunted the vagabond. We couldn't get hold of him, but the intelligence of the dog, and the delighted confidence he imparted to me as he tumbled across the country in the dark, were quite enchanting. Two policemen, appearing in the distance and making a professional show of stealthiness, had a narrow escape. As he was in the act of flying at them, I was obliged to hold him round the neck with both arms and call to the Force to vanish in an inglorious manner."

On another occasion Sultan broke his chain and ran off to have a sort of prize fight with a dog of his own size, weight and age, of whom he was terribly jealous. A frightful battle ensued, and Sultan left his opponent nearly dead. And yet Dickens clung to him. Indeed, no dog ever had such a chance or was more tolerated. But at last it came to a fatal point beyond which toleration could not safely go.

On a summer evening a year after Sultan's arrival, we were all sitting on the porch. My Master was entertaining Harry and Plorn with riddles when a fearful shriek must have pierced the air, for all of a sudden everyone rushed down the steps toward the front gate. To our horror we found Sultan holding onto a little girl, rolling over and over with her in the dust. The sister of one of the servants had come through the gate without ringing the bell, as everyone coming that way was requested to do because of the dogs. Sultan, in trying to prevent her from passing, had made a rush, broken his chain, and fallen upon her. With a fearsome voice Dickens called the dog off, and Sultan came obediently to his master's side. I backed away and sought protection at Plorn's side. The child was rather badly bitten about the thigh and leg, and she was terribly frightened. With a gentle, soothing voice, Dickens calmed her; and lifting her in his arms, he carried her to the house.

The child was well cared for, and she fully recovered. Sultan was not so fortunate. The morning following the attack, Dickens decided that this fierce wilful animal could not be allowed to be a menace any longer. He would have to be taken to the far meadow and shot.

At the end of the day, Dickens again wrote to the giver. "Sultan went to his execution, evidently supposing the procession to be a party detached in pursuit of something to kill or eat. It was very affecting. But observing in the procession a wheelbarrow and a double-barrelled gun, he became meditative, and fixed the bearer of the gun with his eyes. A stone deftly thrown across him by the village blacksmith caused him to look round for an instant, and then he fell dead, shot through the heart."

We did not have long to grieve for Sultan, for shortly after his death there came as another gift to the Master of Gad's Hill a splendid Newfoundland named Don. He was a giant of a dog with a soft black coat and massive head, from which gazed great drooping eyes. He was as gentle as he was large, and equal to Linda in both. They enjoyed each other's company immediately, and so it was that by the spring of 1867 Linda and Don were the proud parents of two puppies. They had their father's black coat, their mother's alert head and the huge feet of both. One of them Dickens named Diogenes after the steadfast kindly dog he had created to be Florence's companion in *Dombey and Son*. The other he named Bumble after the Beadle in *Oliver Twist*, because of a peculiarly pompous and overbearing manner he had of appearing to mount guard over the yard when he was an absolute infant.

Raised by their master in the walking tradition, the two puppies were by late summer as knowledgeable about the Kentish countryside as their parents. Thus on any afternoon the Master of Gad's Hill might be seen in the company of four dogs and a cat striding round Cobham, skirting the park and village, or taking the high street through Rochester past the ancient Norman castle and the splendid cathedral. Often this curious group could be seen sitting in the Master's favourite, peaceful, and secluded churchyard in the village of Shorne, where wild flowers mingled

Charles Dickens with the dogs

with the grass, and the soft landscape around formed a fairy spot in the garden of England.

In November Dickens left our little family and the puppydom he so enjoyed to sail for America. The flag was taken down from the house-top. The Master of Gad's Hill was away from us until May of 1868. In those six months he travelled up and down the eastern part of the country giving readings from his books. People flocked to hear and see him. He was the toast of America. Of course, he revelled in it; the writer and the actor were one. But it was hard on him. It was winter, and he was not well.

He was glad to be coming home, and home was glad he was coming. In fact, Higham villagers were planning to greet him at the station, unhitch Toby and pull their famous neighbour in the carriage up the long hill in triumph to Gad's Hill Place. Knowing this would embarrass my Master, Georgina and Mamie arranged for the basket phaeton pulled by Newman Noggs to meet Dickens at Gravesend, the station before Higham.

A greeting committee just the right size proceeded to the reunion. It consisted of the groom, of course, and me, sitting next to him proudly on the front wicker seat, and Don, Diogenes and Bumble loping alongside.

When our Master alighted from the train, the dogs bounded and tumbled to greet him. I stood on the green cushioned seat and stretched to reach his hand. He gathered me into his lap as he took his seat in the basket phaeton, and we started for home, the dogs coming behind as we trotted along, and lifting their heads to have their ears pulled − a special attention which they received from no one else.

Although we had avoided the boisterous crowds waiting at the Higham station, our route home was a parade for it was marked by flags flying from all the houses and cheering villagers lining the way.

"Welcome home, Mr. Dickens."

"God bless you, sir. May you live to write for ever."

"Three cheers for the Master of Gad's Hill, Charles Dickens."

"Hip, hip, hoorah! Hip, hip, hoorah! Hip, hip, hoorah!"

When we drove into the stable-yard, Linda was greatly excited; weeping profusely and throwing herself on her back that she might caress her master's foot with her great forepaws. Mrs Bouncer barked in the greatest agitation on being called down and tore round and round her master. Georgina, Mamie, Harry and Plorn greeted him eagerly, and the flag was raised atop the house to wave gently in the spring breeze. The head of the household back, life could resume its regular busy pace.

That pace included brisk daily walks. It was on one of these in midsummer that Don and Bumble taught my Master a lesson.

In the summer of 1868 there was a drought, and the ponds and surface wells had become waterless, so Dickens would not let the dogs swim in the canal because the people had to drink of it. But when they got into the River Medway, it was hard to get them out again.

On one such bathing excursion Bumble got into difficulties among some floating timber and became frightened. He flailed his oversized front feet on the water, straining to keep his muzzle above the surface. Logs bumped round him and seemed to gather his great head in a lock. He went under and came up again, free of the lock but sputtering and pawing desperately. I dashed back and forth on the bank, my tail high to tell of danger. Don was standing by his master, shaking off the wet and looking on casually, when all of a sudden he perceived something amiss and went in with a bound and brought Bumble out by the ear. Father had saved son. Scarcely a month later Dickens made a decision to save his son, his beloved youngest son, Plorn.

Dickens's boys were somewhat of a disappointment to their father. The older ones searched for success in such faraway places as India, Australia and America, but success eluded them. Harry may be the exception, doing well at Cambridge.

But it was Plorn whom Dickens most worried about in that summer of 1868. He seemed to be drowning in his studies. He had no aptitude or ambition for them. When my Master had decided that his youngest son should become a farmer in Australia, he confided in me one evening:

"As the boy is fond of animals and of being on horseback, and of moving rapidly through the air, I hope he may take better to the Bush than to Books. Sad as it makes me, I must send him to join his brother, Alfred. I must be like Don and pull my son out of his predicament by his ear."

So it was that on a crisp but bleak September morning, with Don and Bumble trotting alongside as if to confirm my Master in his decision,

Plorn aged 16

Dickens and his dear sixteen-year-old boy sat side by side in the carriage on their way to Higham Station. Both were silent in their sorrow and their bravery. Plorn cradled me in his lap and rolled his fingers under my chin. He had been my most playful companion at Gad's. Together we had climbed trees and stalked hedgehogs.

When we got to the station, father and son embraced, and both gave way to their intense grief, quite oblivious of their surroundings. Plorn, unaccustomed to seeing his father so moved, turned his head away toward the train as it approached the station.

The Station Master lifted the boy's bags into the compartment. Plorn would not relinquish to him the box he carried. It contained a complete set of his father's books. These would be his father to him in faraway New South Wales. One last embrace and the tearful boy climbed into the compartment. Slowly the train pulled out of the station; and then, even more slowly, Toby pulled our carriage up the long hill toward home. My Master took me in his lap, but his hands were quiet under my chin. Don and Bumble solemnly escorted us.

That evening in the Study, I knew better than to put out the candle before my Master had finished writing. At last he laid down his pen and said to me, "Life is half made up of partings. That is what I have written to Plorn in this letter, Puss." And then he read it softly aloud.

"'I need not tell you that I love you dearly and am very sorry in my heart to part with you.'" He went on to encourage Plorn:

"'It is my comfort and sincere conviction that you are going to try the life for which you are best fitted. I think its freedom and wildness more suited to you than any experiment in a study or office would have been. . .What you have always wanted until now is a steady, constant purpose. I therefore exhort you to persevere in a thorough determination to do whatever you have to do, as well as you can do it. I was not so old as you are now, when I first had to win my food, and to do it out of this determination; and I have never slackened in it since.'"

And then my Master gave his son words to live by:

"'Never take a mean advantage of any one in any transaction, and never be hard upon people who are in your power. Try to do to others as you would have them do to you, and do not be discouraged if they fail sometimes.'"

At the end of the letter Dickens wrote:

"'Never abandon the wholesome practice of saying your own private prayers, night and morning. I have never abandoned it myself, and I know the comfort of it. I hope you will always be able to say in after life that you had a kind father. You cannot show your affection for him so well, or make him so happy, as by doing your duty.'

"Ah, well, it is done. Plorn's puppydom is over. He is gone." My Master was silent for a long time, and then in a slow and quiet voice he said, "I shall not see him again." Dickens folded the letter with great deliberation and put it into its envelope, which he addressed to his son, now journeying so far away. After another long silence, my weary Master whispered to me, "Now you may put out the candle." I obeyed, and bereft we sat together in the darkness.

10 Murder in the Meadow

'Get up!'

'It is you, Bill!'

'Get up!!!'

There was a candle burning, but he drew it from the candlestick and hurled it under the grate. Seeing the faint light of early day without, the girl rose to undraw the curtain.

'Let it be. There's light enough for wot I've got to do.'

'Bill, why do you look like that at me?'

The robber regarded her for a few seconds, with dilated nostrils and heaving breast; then, grasping her by the head and throat, dragged her into the middle of the room, and placed his heavy hand upon her mouth.

"For God's sake! Bill!"

'You were watched to-night, you she-devil; every word you said was heard.'

'Then if every word I said was heard, it was heard that I spared you. Bill, dear Bill, you cannot have the heart to kill me. Oh! think of all I have given up, only this one night, for you. Bill, Bill! For dear God's sake, for your own, for mine, stop before you spill my blood!!!'

The shrill pleas of a woman's voice pierced the morning quiet of the Study where I sat with Charley, who had come down from London to do some editing for his father. I had sought Charley's company when my Master had forbidden me to follow him to the meadow after our usual morning rounds.

What was I hearing now? How was I hearing it? Who was about to be murdered? Where were these dreadful voices coming from? Charley started from his chair and dashed to the window to locate the victim and her assailant. He must have thought to save her, but there was no one on the high road. The fearful pleadings were coming from the back of the house. They rose louder and louder as Charley tore through the hall, out of the back door and onto the lawn. Suddenly he stopped so short that I, being close on his heels, tumbled right into him. What did he see? I got to my feet and looked up at his staring face. His eyes led mine to the far end of the meadow. There, waving his arms wildly and striding up and down was my Master. The dreadful voices were his.

> The housebreaker freed one arm, and grasped his pistol. The certainty of immediate detection if he fired, flashed across his mind; and he beat it twice upon the upturned face that almost touched his own.
>
> She staggered and fell, but raising herself on her knees, she drew from her bosom a white handkerchief – Rose Maylie's – and holding it up towards Heaven, breathed one prayer, for mercy to her Maker.
>
> It was a ghastly figure to look upon. The murderer, staggering backward to the wall, and shutting out the sight with his hand, seized a heavy club, and struck her down!!

It *was* a ghastly figure to look upon. Charley and I stood transfixed while Dickens played out the scene, violently acting the parts of murderer and murdered, and narrating it all with fearsome gestures. The hair on my arched back and bushed tail stood stiffer than it had in Cooling church-yard when Pip stumbled on his convict. Finally, but before the scene was finished, and unseen by his father, Charley turned and made his way back to the house. My place was not with my Master at this moment. It was for good reason that he had not allowed me to follow him to the meadow. Seeking the reassurance of Charley's company, I hurried to catch up with him as he returned to the Study.

Charley, who was proving most valuable in his editorial duties for his father at his weekly magazine "All the Year Round," travelled down to Gad's Hill when he could. We were glad of his visits, because with Plorn gone to Australia and Harry beginning his studies at Cambridge, our family was smaller than ever before – just Dickens, Georgina and Mamie in residence. Although neither could bring himself to outright words of affection, it was good for father and son to sit together after dinner and discuss matters of business and the affairs of England's empire.

This evening the minds of both father and son were focused on the morning's murder in the meadow. On the table between them in the Study my Master had placed a copy of *Oliver Twist*. Now he took it in his hands and opened it in one movement. Quietly and also in one movement, I took its place on the table.

"I have made a short reading of the murder in *Oliver Twist*," Dickens began slowly. "I cannot make up my mind, however, whether to do it or not. I have no doubt that I could petrify an audience by carrying out the notion I have of the way of rendering it. But whether the impression would be so horrible as to keep them away another time, is what I cannot satisfy myself upon."

Charley moved uneasily in his chair. He must have then told his father what he had seen and heard in the morning, for Dickens leaned forward eagerly and inquired, "What do you think?"

Again Charley adjusted his position in the chair. He shook his head slowly as he answered his father.

My Master did not like his son's reply, for he stood bolt upright and moved to the fireplace.

"'Don't do it'? What do you mean by 'Don't do it'? You say it is the finest thing you have ever heard, but I should not do it?"

Charley would not engage his father any further on the subject. I knew why he had made bold to speak his opinion; he, his sisters and Georgina were very worried about Dickens's health. I saw their anxious faces when he limped or became dizzy and had to sit down. The reading tours he had thrown himself into, beginning years before in 1858, were now taking their toll on him. This reading of Sikes killing Nancy, this ghastly horror, acted out so dramatically by Dickens surely would shock his nervous system beyond repair. But Charley knew better than to attribute his disapproval of the murder reading to the matter of health. His father would not hear it. So a dutiful son gave no reason for saying, "Don't do it."

Dickens stood gazing into the fire, his face drawn and tired, his right hand leaning on the mantel and supporting weight enough to relieve his foot. Charley, for want of something to fill the awkward minutes, reached out and stroked me. Finally Dickens relieved the strained atmosphere by inquiring about his grandchildren. Charley, who had been married in 1861, had five children in the intervening seven years. They were their grandfather's delight. "Another generation begins to peer above the table," he had said to me after a visit by the young family. So father and son spoke of Mekitty and little Charles and their bright beginnings, and not of Nancy and Sikes and their dark endings.

★ ★ ★ ★ ★

When Charley left us to go to bed, both the fire and the candle were burning low. I reached forward and put out the latter while my Master stirred up the former.

"There is enough log left to warm us as I tell you about these readings of mine, Puss." My Master pulled his chair closer to the hearth and lifted me onto his lap as he sat down. "Though they worry my family and friends, they bring me great pleasure. And, I believe, they bring me as much fame as do my books. They come from my books. I've worked up passages from sixteen of my stories; the murder from *Oliver Twist* would make seventeen. In ten years I've given almost four hundred performances. 'Dickens is coming!' they shout in the streets of the cities where I am booked to read. I must add evenings to satisfy the crowds.

"The demand is no less in cities far away than it is in London. Once in Edinburgh in a gale of wind and a fierce rain, a thousand people had to be turned away. There was no getting into the hall, no getting out, no possibility of getting rid of them. It was a raving mob I had to calm. And calm them I did by making space for the ladies to sit around me on the platform, and by promising those on the outside another Reading.

"The people always respond to me and a good thing, for one night it saved us from a dreadful tragedy. In Newcastle, where the crowd was crammed in three galleries approached by a steep flight of stairs, the gas flame batten over the platform came crashing down. The noise was terrifying, and a lady in the front row screamed and ran wildly toward me. For an instant a panic seemed about to break out. Gathering my wits, I smiled and called out to her in a calm voice, 'There's nothing the matter,

Charles Dickens, the reader

I assure you; don't be alarmed, pray sit down.' She trusted me and returned to her seat, and the place broke out in great cheers. Meanwhile my men had set about to smother the flames on stage and mend the batten so I could proceed.

"And then I was drawn back to America a year ago to give over seventy Readings in sixteen cities. I needed to go back, because in 1842 I went with Catherine, spending six months travelling as far as St Louis by rail, coach, river steamer and canal boat. We could not take the children of course and Daniel Maclise did a crayon drawing of them for us. I recorded the findings of that first visit to that young republic and angered its citizens. Although I praised much of what I saw, I was surprised and grieved by the poverty, the institutions and prisons I found. I was disappointed by the corrupt politicians and rowdy press. And I was horrified by the evils of slavery.

"I further angered the Americans when I sent off my character Martin Chuzzlewit to that country, so that he might become the victim of the vulgar, boastful, fraudulent men of business, who were so quickly rising

First visit to America, 1842. Left to right: Katie, Walter,
Charley, Mamie and Grip, the raven

The British lion in America

there. I thought I needed to make peace twenty-five years later, but I found the country changed for the better and holding no grudge.

"No grudge at all, and willing to stand in a queue (they call it a line in America) all night to buy tickets to hear me. It was Boston first. Tickets went on sale for my first reading on a Monday a fortnight prior to the event. The human file began at seven-thirty on Sunday evening. Temperature below freezing. By midnight over a hundred people had come. Many sat in chairs they had brought; many stretched out on the pavement on blankets or mattresses. As the queue grew longer, it grew merrier. People shouldered up against each other and stamped their feet for warmth. Strangers became friends. They sang songs, told stories. One man, I understand, made a spirited speech: 'Gentlemen, there are but three men who have stamped themselves upon the civilization of the nineteenth century. Those men, gentlemen, are Charles Shakespeare, William Dickens and – myself.' And with a reeling bow, he tumbled into the street.

"Best thing about that queue, dear Puss, was the mankind in it. As listed by a journalist, they were 'truckmen, porters, clerks, roughs, clergymen, merchants, gamblers, speculators, gentlemen, loafers, white men, black men, coloured men, boys and three women! Broadcloth, no cloth! Fine linen, doubtful linen, no linen! The lion stood up with the lamb.'

"I have always felt a peculiar responsibility to such as these. Never miss a performance except when I am defeated by an old ailment or new attack of pain. This American trip was a trial. The work was hard: long, bone-rattling journeys, vast halls holding thousands. The climate was hard: mountainous snow, treacherous ice. The life was hard: sleepless nights, a frightful cold that would not be shaken. But the gain was enormous. And then home and start it all again in my own country.

"Why? you ask, why all this on top of my book writing, my magazine editing, my family tending? I have told you on another evening. There is a fire in me that burns to be doing. And then, too, there is still that magic of the stage. Standing in the garish gas lights with expectant faces turned up to me, I am no longer Charles Dickens, sickly child, blacking factory boy, driven writer, wishful thinker. I am bent, tight-fisted Scrooge and timid trembling Bob Cratchit, and round merry-legged Fezziwig. I speak in the hard metallic voice of Dombey and the high tired voice of his little son, Paul, and the most snappish angry voice of Mrs Pipchin. I gently pat the velvet top of my reading desk, and it becomes the head of a child in need of consoling. That same desk-top I slam violently as the ferocious Squeers brings his wretched schoolboys to order. In short,

I am my characters, Puss. They and I are so at one with our audience that I am powerless to do other than laugh when those upturned faces laugh, and cry when they cry.

"It is that responsibility and that oneness that make me want to give my audiences more and more. That is why I must do the murder, Puss. Sikes must kill Nancy. It is decided, no matter if others, including son Charley, think those fatal blows will deal me a fatal blow."

The fire was reduced to a scattering of glowing red embers now. Every now and then it blazed up briefly as small mounds of hot ash crumbled apart. The glow and warmth of its inexorable dying held us in their spell. In a voice almost a whisper, my Master said wearily, "The fire consumes itself, my dear Puss. Let us retire before it is out. I want no omens of the fire in me."

11   Venerables and the Queen

With Plorn in Australia and Harry at Cambridge, I might have lacked playmates. Not at all. That new generation that had begun to peer above the table in 1862 was by 1870 six strong. When their father, Charley, brought them for a visit, they filled the bedrooms of Gad's Hill. Once again miniature mallets knocked croquet balls through hoops and under rose bushes, little feet scurried up and down the staircase, and Newman Noggs was bell-harnessed to pull the basket-phaeton full of giggling children.

Just as he had been the most devoted and entertaining father, so too was Charles Dickens the most loving and indulgent grandfather. In return for all the merriment he provided, Dickens exacted only one thing of his little troop, and this with a twinkle in his eye:

"Mekitty, as you are the oldest, a very old and respected eight, you must see to it that your brothers and sisters call me Venerables, Wenerables if it is easier. Their infant lives will not be worth five minutes' purchase if they call me grandpa. My name is Wenerables to them and to you."

Mekitty, in her devotion, managed Venerables quite easily. Little Charles, who was six, preferred Wenerables, and the four baby sisters variously translated it to Wenbull, Winible, and most heart-warming of all to my Master, Wenapple.

Their father's birthday being on Twelfth Night, January sixth, the troop was brought to Gad's for a proper party in the style of those joyful celebrations of years earlier. In those days, when Charley was a lad, Dickens had bought up the box of tricks of a conjuror who was going out of business. He had set himself to master every sleight of hand and had become a prestidigitator of phenomenal reputation. Now he revived his show in the dining room at the end of dinner before dessert, to a

The Master as Conjuror

whole new audience of spellbound children – and spellbound cat. Before our very eyes he made coins fly through the air, turned watches into tea-caddies, turned ladies' handkerchiefs into candies, retrieved more candies from behind children's ears, caused Mekitty's tiny china doll to vanish and then reappear with a message for her – "Mekitty, hug the kitty" – which she immediately did, to my delight. Also to my delight, my Master turned a box of bran into a guinea pig. Before I could lay claim to this nose-wiggling creature, little Charles snatched it up for himself. And then the great magician performed his final act. Turning a black top hat upside down, he poured into it raw eggs, flour and a bowl of ingredients, lighted a match, and in a matter of seconds produced a fully cooked, steaming plum pudding as Charley's birthday tribute.

The next time we were visited by this merry band was in early March. Winter was relinquishing its grip on the land, and Venerables chose a sunny afternoon to conduct the two oldest children on a short walk. Although he would never admit it, my Master was glad of the small

99

Mamie reads to Mekitty

strides of his young companions. His left leg, indeed his whole left side, pained him. He had confessed to me the evening before the children's arrival that his weakness and deadness were all in the left side, and if he didn't look at anything he tried to touch with his left hand, he didn't know where it was. "But," he hastened to add, "we will not alarm the family with a word of this."

Accompanied by the dogs, we travelled down the lane that bordered the property. When it began to wind too far away from home, my Master turned his company back toward the meadow. Once safely in the middle of this great space, Mekitty and little Charles let go of their grandfather's hands and romped with Bumble. Their play was interrupted by the sound of the bell in the cupola, atop the house.

"It must be something important, children. The bell is ringing, Puss. Come, let's go see." The children scrambled to claim Venerables's hands and, full company abreast, we crossed the meadow. As we approached the house, the grown-up part of the family – Georgina, Mamie, Charley and his wife, Bessie – appeared at the door.

"What prompts this gladsome summons?" inquired my Master. Smiling silence answered him. Then Charley stepped forward and held out to his father a most important-looking letter with a great wax seal upon it. The little hands relinquished their hold, and Dickens stepped forward to take the letter. As he cracked the seal to reveal the contents, all eyes were upon him. Mekitty and little Charles stretched to see the elegant writing.

"Why, it's an invitation from the Queen, a summons to Buckingham Palace to a private audience with Her Majesty Queen Victoria. Now what do you think of that?"

We all thought it quite splendid. Mekitty clapped her hands and jumped up and down; little Charles followed suit, as it was his habit to mimic his big sister in her joyful activities. Their parents and Georgina and Mamie passed the invitation eagerly from one to the other and back again. As they admired it, I admired its recipient by rubbing back and forth against Dickens's good right leg. Imagine, my Master going to see the Queen!

"I will respond that I would be proud and happy to wait upon Her Majesty. And I think I will make a little jest that Her Majesty might take the opportunity to make her humble servant a baronet. We will have 'Of Gad's Hill Place' attached to the title of the baronetcy, please – on account of the divine William Shakespeare and Falstaff making this place so famous.

"Wot larks! Wot larks!" my Master repeated merrily, as he disappeared back into the house to write his acceptance and his little jest.

March 9 was the appointed day. What visions played in the family's heads as Dickens departed from Gad's Hill for Buckingham Palace, I do not know. I could picture my Master, handsomely – even dashingly – attired, as was his habit from his youthful dapper days. Even though the springing stride which had carried him at the rate of four miles an hour on his walks had departed now, he still cut an imposing figure. In my mind's eye I could see him standing before the Queen. And from a portrait I once glimpsed of her, I could see her surrounded by her nine children and her over-large collection of dogs.

How hard it was to wait for my Master's return! But return he did; and although he dragged one leg rather wearily, he was in high spirits. We gathered round him as he settled into his armchair in the drawing room. Dickens lifted his throbbing foot onto the ottoman, and the children snugged up on either side of his ankle. Mamie lifted me onto her lap and sat forward in her chair eagerly, and our favourite raconteur began his telling:

Queen Victoria presents her book to Dickens

"Our Queen is like a girl in manner, although strangely shy. You would be surprised at our conversation, my dears. It was much more of cabbages than kings. We talked of the plight of the poor, of my trip to America and of American ways. Her Majesty spoke happily of seeing me thirteen years ago acting in 'The Frozen Deep'. She kindly reminded me that my Gracious Sovereign was so pleased that when the curtain fell she sent round begging me to come and see her and accept her thanks. I replied that I was in my Farce dress (for that was the second play on the bill) and must beg to be excused. Whereupon she sent again, saying that the dress 'could not be so ridiculous as that'. . . I sent my duty in reply, but again hoped Her Majesty would have the kindness to excuse my presenting myself in a costume and appearance that were not my own. She allowed that she had been quite taken by my pride and determination, an unprecedented thing to turn down a royal request. I allowed that I could not appear before Her Majesty tired and hot, with the paint still upon my face, in an absurd wig and red nose. And so we laughed about that evening and went on to talk about the price of butcher's meat.

"We were alone in our meeting," Dickens continued, much to my astonishment: where, I said to myself, were all the children and the bevy of dogs? "Court etiquette, of course, did not allow me to sit down, swollen foot or not, because the Queen remained standing, leaning on the arm of a sofa throughout the entire hour and a half of the interview. I would have fallen before admitting to my pain. And then I would have found myself in such an ignoble posture that lying prostrate before her I would have had to feign supplication or adoration. It might have proved ludicrous and worthy of another laugh. Of course," my Master added with a twinkle in his eye, "in such a posture I could have received the touch of the sword on each shoulder and thus my baronetcy. Ah, I am relieved to say none of that came to pass – not even the baronetcy. No, I will remain what I have always been, Charles Dickens.

"Her Majesty did do me the honour of presenting me with an autographed copy of her *Journal of Our Life in the Highlands*, saying kindly that the humblest of writers would be ashamed to offer it to the greatest. She then asked for a set of my works. I shall send her a set in red morocco and gold. Yes, that is what I shall do."

And with that Dickens bade his family good-night, kissed the sleepy-headed children and rose to go to his Study. I followed; I knew he had more to tell me.

★ ★ ★ ★ ★

When my Master closed the Study door after us, instead of going directly to his chair, he went to the bookcase that held a set of his works. He pulled several from the long line and carried them to the table next to his chair. I took my place between them and the candle.

"I shall light the candle so you can put it out, but you won't want to put it out till I tell you to do so. I have some good story pieces to read to you."

As my Master struck the match to the wick, the knob on the Study door turned. Ever so slowly and silently, a small boy, hands reaching above his head to grasp the knob, pushed open the door and, just as deliberately and quietly taking the knob on this side, shut it behind him. Making his way across the room on tiny bare feet under his nightshirt, little Charles climbed into his Wenerables's lap. Gathering his grandson to him with enfolding arms and the gentlest of smiles, Dickens said softly to me, "It appears we have company for tonight's story, dear Puss. That is as it should be, for my tale draws near its end, and I would bring it full circle.

Evidence suggests that this is Charley's son

It started with a child of half a century ago. I would have all such children today and tomorrow better off for what that child became and did. This little Charles will grow up in a better England than did his namesake, that boy of the blacking factory.

"Our Queen will give her name to an age of great change. And I have helped. I write to increase the stock of harmless cheerfulness and to show that virtue may be found in the by-ways of the world, that it is not incompatible with poverty and rags. Every effort of my pen has been intended to elevate the masses of society and give them the station they deserve among mankind. It has been my children, the children of my brain, who have done the work. Their plight has awakened a nation." My Master took one arm from around the nodding boy and lifted a book from the table.

"This was the first. In these pages lives an orphaned boy named Oliver Twist. Brought up in a workhouse, he was the victim of a systematic course of deception and treachery, known as the Poor Laws. These seemed designed to discourage the poor from seeking refuge in a workhouse by the simple act of starving them to death." And then my Master opened the book and read:

> The room in which the boys were fed was a large stone hall, with
> a copper at one end, out of which the master, dressed in an apron

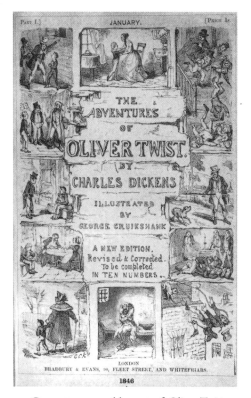

Cover to a monthly part of *Oliver Twist*

for the purpose, and assisted by one or two women, ladled the gruel at meal-times. Of this festive composition each boy had one porringer, and no more. . . The bowls never wanted washing. The boys polished them with the spoons till they shone again; and when they had performed this operation (which never took very long, the spoons being nearly as large as the bowls), they would sit staring at the copper with such eager eyes as if they could have devoured the very bricks of which it was composed, employing themselves, meanwhile, in sucking their fingers most assiduously, with the view of catching up any stray splashes of gruel that might have been cast thereon. Boys have generally excellent appetites. Oliver Twist and his companions suffered the tortures of slow starvation for three months; at last they got so voracious and wild with hunger that one boy, who was tall for his age, and hadn't been used to that sort of thing (for his father had kept a small cook's shop), hinted darkly to his companions that unless he had another basin of gruel *per diem*, he was afraid he might some night happen to eat the boy who slept next him, who happened to be a weakly youth of tender age. He had a wild, hungry eye, and they implicitly believed him. A council was held; lots were cast who should walk up to the master after supper that evening and ask for more; and it fell to Oliver Twist.

The evening arrived; the boys took their places. The master, in his cook's uniform, stationed himself at the copper; his pauper assistants ranged themselves behind him; the gruel was served out, and a long grace was said over the short commons. The gruel disappeared; the boys whispered to each other, and winked at Oliver, while his next neighbours nudged him. Child as he was, he was desperate with hunger, and reckless with misery. He rose from the table, and advancing to the master, basin and spoon in hand, said, somewhat alarmed at his own temerity:

'Please sir, I want some more.'

The master was a fat, healthy man, but he turned very pale. He gazed in stupefied astonishment on the small rebel for some seconds, and then clung for support to the copper. The assistants were paralysed with wonder, the boys with fear.

"Please, sir, I want some more."

'What!' said the master at length, in a faint voice.

'Please, sir,' replied Oliver, 'I want some more.'

The master aimed a blow at Oliver's head with the ladle, pinioned him in his arms, and shrieked aloud for the beadle.

The board were sitting in solemn conclave when Mr. Bumble rushed into the room in great excitement, and addressing the gentleman in the high chair, said:

'Mr. Limbkins, I beg your pardon, sir! Oliver Twist has asked for more!'

There was a general start. Horror was depicted on every countenance. . .

'That boy will be hung,' said the gentleman in the white waistcoat. 'I know that boy will be hung.'

Nobody controverted the prophetic gentleman's opinion. An animated discussion took place. Oliver was ordered into instant confinement; and a bill was next morning pasted on the outside of the gate, offering a reward of five pounds to anybody who would take Oliver Twist off the hands of the parish. In other words, five pounds and Oliver Twist were offered to any man or woman who wanted an apprentice to any trade, business, or calling.

My Master closed the book, put it on the table and cupped his hand round the back of Charles's sleeping blond head.

"Oliver narrowly escaped being apprenticed to a chimney sweep, Puss. That was a wicked job, for little boys no bigger than this one in my lap were sent down tall, narrow chimneys where they frequently became stuck or were suffocated. Oliver was apprenticed to an undertaker, but after being beaten and shut in the basement, he ran away to London. There, in order to reveal the horrors of the life led by the most criminal and degraded of London's population, I introduced my Oliver to a boy pickpocket, the Artful Dodger, who in turn introduced him to the sinister Fagin and his den of boy-thieves. It was my intention to take the romance and fun out of the life of thieves, so the fortunate, my readers, could see the horrors of the unfortunate. With innocent Oliver trapped in this life, I endeavoured to paint the luckless criminals in all their deformity, in all their wretchedness, in all the squalid misery of their lives; to show them as they really were, for ever skulking uneasily through the dirtiest paths of life, with the great, black, ghastly gallows closing up their prospect, turn them where they might; it appeared to me that to do this would be to attempt something which was needed, and which would be a service to society. And I did it as best I could. The public responded; the Poor Laws were amended. But there is ever so much more to do, dear Puss.

"While I was writing *Oliver Twist*, I went on a secret pilgrimage to Yorkshire to see firsthand the notorious boarding schools run by brutal, fraudulent masters. The sole purpose of these men was to get as much from the parents as possible and give as little to the boys as possible. These boys seemed to be abandoned by their families. So while still writing *Oliver Twist*, I began my second book against the evils that threatened childhood. This is it, Puss, *The Life and Adventures of Nicholas Nickleby*." Here my Master took a second book from the table.

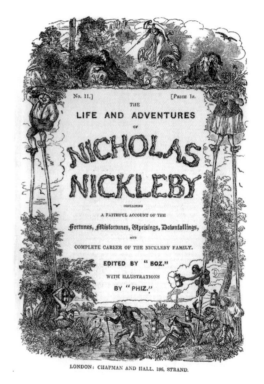

Cover of a monthly part of *Nicholas Nickleby*

"Our hero in this is not a child, but a young man very nearly nineteen, open, handsome and ingenuous. Nicholas Nickleby, owing to the untimely death of his father, must earn his living; so he takes a position as assistant to Wackford Squeers, the Yorkshire schoolmaster of Dotheboys Hall. Note the names, dear Puss, for I chose them, as indeed I do all my names, with great care, that my readers might take pleasure in their hints." My Master said this with a wink and then began to read.

EDUCATION – At Mr Wackford Squeers's Academy, Dotheboys Hall, at the delightful; village of Dotheboys, near Greta Bridge in Yorkshire, Youth are boarded, clothed, booked, furnished with pocket-money, provided with all necessaries, instructed in all languages living and dead, mathematics, orthography, geometry, astronomy, trigonom-etry, the use of the globes, algebra, single-stick (if required), writing, arithmetic, fortification, and every other branch of classical literature. Terms twenty guineas per annum. No extras, no vacations, and diet unparalleled. Mr Squeers is in town, and attends daily, from one to four, at the Saracen's Head, Snow Hill. N.B. – An able assistant wanted. Annual salary £5. A Master of Arts would be preferred.

This advertisement appeared in *The Times, Morning Post, Chronicle, Herald* and *Advertiser*.

The fanlight, 48 Doughty Street

"And our hero, although no Master of Arts, was made to take the job by his uncle and go down to Dotheboys with the schoolmaster.

> Mr. Squeers's appearance was not prepossessing. He had but one eye, and the popular prejudice runs in favour of two. The eye he had was unquestionably useful, but decidedly not ornamental: being of a greenish grey, and in shape resembling the fan-light of a street door. The blank side of his face was wrinkled and puckered up, which gave him a very sinister appearance, especially when he smiled, at which time his expression bordered closely on the villainous.

"Nicholas very quickly finds out that Wackford Squeers, his wife, Mrs Squeers, his daughter Fanny Squeers and son, Master Wackford Squeers are a brutal, rapacious and ignorant family and treat the boys worse than their animals. And so, very soon, he turns on the schoolmaster and gives him a thorough-going beating and decamps with one of the poor boys, Smike. This results in that remarkable letter written to Nicholas's uncle by Fanny Squeers:

Nicholas beats Squeers

Dotheboys Hall, Thursday Morning.

SIR

My pa requests me to write to you, the doctors considering it doubtful whether he will ever recuvver the use of his legs which prevents
his holding a pen.

We are in a state of mind beyond everything, and my pa is one
mask of brooses both blue and green likewise two forms are steepled
in his Goar. We were kimpelled to have him carried down into the
kitchen where he now lays. You will judge from this that he had
been brought very low.

When your nevvew that you recommended for a teacher had
done this to my pa and jumped upon his body with his feet and
also lkangwedge which I will not pollewt my pen with describing,
he assaulted my ma with dreadful violence, dashed her to the earth,
and drove her back comb several inches into her head. A very little
more and it must have entered her skull. We have a medical certi-
fiket that if it had, the tortershell would have effectd the brain.

Me and my brother were then the victims of his feury since which
we have suffered very much which leads us to the arrowing belief
that we have received some injury in our insides, especially as no
marks of violence are visible externally. I am screaming out loud all
the time I write and so is my brother which takes off my attention
rather and I hope will excuse mistakes.

The monster having sasiated his thirst for blood ran away, taking
with him a boy of desperate character that he excited to rebellyon,
and a garnet ring belonging to my ma, and not having been appre-
hended by the constables is supposed to have been took up by some
stage-coach. My ma begs that if he comes to you the ring may be
returned, and that you will let the thief and assassin go, as if we
prosecute him he would only be transported, and if he is let go he
is sure to be hung before long which will save us trouble and be
much more satisfactory. Hoping to hear from you when convenient
    I remain, Yours and cetrer

FANNY SQUEERS.

P.S. – I pity his ignorance and despise him."

"And as Squeers so aptly says: 'HERE'S RICHES!'

"The five year old brother of Richard Hughes, author of Tom Brown's
Schooldays, was read Nicholas Nickleby as it came out in its monthly
parts, and was disappointed that Nicholas and the boys had not been
rewarded, nor had Squeers and his family been punished, and had a letter
written to tell me so.

"I was very busy then; but immediately sat down and wrote back:

111

Doughty Street, London   12th December 1838

"Respected Sir,

I have given Squeers one cut on the neck and two on the head, at which he appeared much surprised and began to cry, which, being a cowardly thing, is just what I should have expected from him wouldn't you? I have carefully done what you told me in your letter about the lamb and the two "sheeps" for the little boys. They have also had some good ale and porter, and some wine. I am sorry you didn't say what wine you would like them to have. I gave them some sherry which they liked very much, except one boy, who was a little sick and choked a good deal. He was rather greedy, and that's the truth, and I believe it went the wrong way, which I say served him right, and I hope you will say so too. Nicholas had his roast lamb as you said he was to, but he could not eat it all, and says if you do not mind his doing so he should like to have the rest hashed tomorrow with some greens, which he is very fond of, and so am I. He said he did not like to have his porter hot, for he thought it spoilt the flavour, so I let him have it cold. You should have seen him drink it. I thought he would never have left off. I also gave him three pounds in money, all in sixpences, to make it seem more, and he said directly that he should give more than half to his mam and sister, and divide the rest with poor Smike, and I say he is a good fellow for saying so; and if anybody says he isn't I am ready to fight him whenever they like – there!

Fanny Squeers shall be attended to, depend upon it. Your drawing of her is very like, except that I don't think the hair is quite curly enough. The nose is particularly like hers, and so are the legs. She is a nasty disagreeable thing, and I know that it will make her very cross when she sees it; and what I say is that I hope it may. You will say the same I know – at least I think you will.

I meant to have written you a long letter, but I cannot write very fast when I like the person I am writing to, because that makes me think about them, and I like you, and so I tell you. Besides, it is just eight o'clock at night, and I always go to bed at eight o'clock, except when it is my birthday, and then I sit up to supper. So I will not say anything more besides this – and that is my love to you and Neptune; and if you will drink my health every Christmas Day, I will drink yours – come.

I am, Respected Sir, Your affectionate friend

P.S. – I don't write my name very plain, but you know what it is.

   You know, So never mind."

I sent it to the Reverend Barham, saying: 'Accept a thousand thanks for the epistle, which found me cogitating the next number of Nicholas, and instantly took me away from it to write an answer, which I enclose. I send it open for your edification, but when you have read it pray seal it with a very large seal in order that it may bear an appearance of becoming form and gravity. The communication to which it is a reply, has amused me very much.'

"Once I had exposed those Yorkshire schools they could not last long and didn't.

"The monstrous neglect of education in England and the disregard of it by the State, as a means of forming good or bad citizens and miserable or happy men, is on its way to repair.

"So, too was this country's cruel way of dealing with a man in debt. In this book, *Little Dorrit*," here my Master exchanged the book in his hand for another from the table, "I recreated a setting close to the bone.

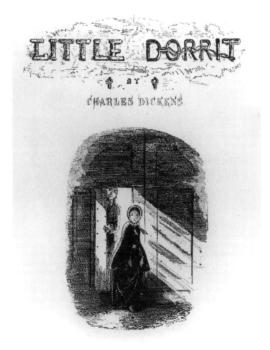

A title page from *Little Dorrit*

My heart aches to think of the debtors' prison. Only you, my evening confidant, know about my father's months imprisoned in the Marshalsea, with his wife and children in misery with him. I could come and go from them, for I was 'free' to earn the family money in the blacking factory. But this child, Little Dorrit, had no place to go.

> At what period of her early life, the little creature began to perceive that it was not the habit of all the world to live locked up in narrow yards surrounded by high walls with spikes at the top, would be a difficult question to settle. But she was a very, very little creature indeed, when she had somehow gained the knowledge, that her clasp of her father's hand was to be always loosened at the door which the great key opened; and that while her own light steps were free to pass beyond it, his feet must never cross that line. A pitiful and plaintive look, with which she had begun to regard him when she was still extremely young, was perhaps a part of this discovery.
>
> With a pitiful and plaintive look for everything indeed, but with something in it for only him that was like protection, this Child of the Marshalsea and child of the Father of the Marshalsea, sat by her

The walls of the Marshalsea prison for debt

friend the turnkey in the lodge, kept the family room, or wandered about the prison-yard, for the first eight years of her life. With a pitiful and plaintive look for her wayward sister; for her idle brother; for the high blank walls; for the faded crowd they shut in; for the games of the prison children as they whooped and ran, and played at hide-and-seek, and made the iron bars of the inner gateway 'Home.'

Exercise ground in the Marshalsea

Wistful and wondering, she would sit in summer weather by the high fender in the lodge, looking up at the sky through the barred window, until bars of light would arise, when she turned her eyes away, between her and her friend, and she would see him through a grating, too.

'Thinking of the fields,' the turnkey said once, after watching her, 'ain't you?'

'Where are they?' she inquired.

'Why, they're – over there, my dear,' said the turnkey with a vague flourish of his key. 'Just about there.'

'Does anybody open them, and shut them? Are they locked?'

The turnkey was discomfited. 'Well,' he said, 'Not in general.'

'Are they very pretty, Bob?' She called him Bob, by his own particular request and instruction.

'Lovely. Full of flowers. There's buttercups, and there's daisies, and there's' – the turnkey hesitated, being short of floral nomenclature – 'there's dandelions, and all manner of games.'

'Is it very pleasant to be there, Bob?'

'Prime,' said the turnkey.

'Was father ever there?'

'Hem!' coughed the turnkey. 'O yes, he was there, sometimes.'

'Is he sorry not to be there now?'

'N – not particular,' said the turnkey.

'Nor any of the people?' she asked, glancing at the listless crowd within. 'O, are you quite sure and certain, Bob?'

At this difficult point of the conversation Bob gave in, and changed the subject to hard-bake: always his last resource when he found his little friend getting him into a political, social, or theological corner. But this was the origin of a series of Sunday excursions that these two curious companions made together. They used to issue from the lodge on alternate Sunday afternoons with great gravity, bound for some meadows or green lanes that had been elaborately appointed by the turnkey in the course of the week; and there she picked grass and flowers to bring home, while he smoked his pipe. Afterwards, there were tea-gardens, shrimps, ale, and other delicacies; and then they would come back hand in hand, unless she was more than usually tired, and had fallen asleep on his shoulder.

With a sigh my Master closed the book. "The Marshalsea is gone. Should you go on a walk with me in London to the place where it was, you will find your little feet on the very paving-stones of the extinct Marshalsea jail; will see its narrow yard to the right and to the left, very little altered if at all, except that the walls were lowered when the place got free; will look upon the rooms in which the debtors lived; will stand among the crowding ghosts of many miserable years.

"So that brings us near full circle. Much work accomplished." My Master replaced the book on top of the others next to me and patted the stack.

"I must say, dear Puss, these books are good stories which make their readers think twice. They pricked a conscience and an imagination. We would tenderly cherish that light of Fancy which is inherent in the human breast; which according to its nurture burns with an inspiring flame, or sinks into a sullen glare, but which (or woe betide the day!) can never be extinguished.

"Now that's unlike this candle, is it not, my dear little fireman?" He lifted his hand from the books and took my paw. "Or should I say, my dear old fireman? You did not know what you were asking for when you put out that first candle ten years ago, did you? Well, put this one out now. We will sit here together, the three of us, a little while longer."

I obeyed with pleasure, and we shared the dark: a sleeping child, a master's cat, and a venerable author who had visited a queen and made her realm a better place. Little wonder a host of grandchildren would call Charles Dickens 'Venerables', which he said, "They sincerely believe to be my name and a kind of title that I have received from a grateful country." While I thought back on it all, the little boy dreamed his dreams – and my Master, no doubt, dreamed his.

The Last
12 Improvement

The summer of 1870 was an exceptionally beautiful one, and the house had never looked prettier, or the gardens brighter or more full of flowers. The Master of Gad's Hill was forever making improvements to his little Kentish freehold. His daughter Katie teased him lovingly about each alteration in the house: walls torn down, rooms added, attic story raised for bedrooms. Dickens revelled in it all. When he extended the drawing room by removing the fireplace wall, two girders had to be put into place to support the chimney breast in the upper stories. He reported to a friend:

"Two girders were both got up by eight o'clock at night. It was ticklish work – nine men gasping, snuffing, heaving, snorting, balancing themselves on bricks and tumbling over each other. But it really was well done, and with great cheerfulness and spirit. Nothing has fallen down or blown up since. Yawning chasms abound, and dust obscures all objects, but we hope to weather it."

Of course, I was in the midst of it all, doing my own balancing on the girders and tumbling through the new opening between the drawing room and dining room, becoming a dusty grey rather than a brown tiger cat.

In 1870 with the drawing-room thus extended, my Master embarked on what he promised Katie would be "positively the last improvement to Gad's Hill": the building of a glass conservatory which opened into both the drawing and dining rooms. Its glass roof allowed sky to be part of the house's architecture and sun to be part of its warmth. To my delight, for it provided me with a hunting cat's jungle, Dickens filled this room with great green leafy plants and creepers which he hoped some day to see covering the glass ceiling with bright flowers.

Katie mightily approved of this sunny room. On a visit the first weekend in June, she admired it with her proud father; and after dinner was over on Sunday they remained sitting together in the dining room,

His last improvement, the conservatory

gazing into the warm, sweetly scented night air of the conservatory. I joined them, this time choosing to curl up in the full and soft silk of Katie's lap. While Mamie played the piano in the drawing-room, father and daughter talked as they never had before, openly and tenderly.

"Katie, I have a capital set of plots working in *The Mystery of Edwin Drood*. I have high hopes for this novel if, please God, I live to finish it." In quick response to Katie's startled look, he added, "I say 'if', because you know, my dear child, I have not been strong lately." Katie had noticed that his face had rather a grey colour and that he had got very tired after his walk with the dogs and me that afternoon.

Dickens dropped into a philosophical mood. "Man is but mortal, and there is a point beyond which human courage cannot extend. One can only work on, you know – work while it is day." Then gently and remorsefully he said, "But I do wish, Katie, that I had been a better father and a better man."

Katie lifted me from her lap and moved to her father. As she kissed his forehead, she lowered me into his lap, and I joined in consoling this man we loved, who suddenly seemed so grey-haired, careworn, and so absent and absorbed in his thoughts.

The stars above the conservatory glimmered and faded, relinquishing the night sky to summer's early dawn before father and daughter finally went upstairs and I retired to the Study.

119

By the time Katie arose the next morning, the Master of Gad's Hill and I were already at work in the chalet. Dickens had put mirrors in the chalet, and they reflected and refracted, in all kinds of ways, the leaves that quivered at the windows, and the great fields of waving corn, and the sail-dotted river. Our room was high among the branches of the trees; and the birds and the butterflies flew in and out, and the green branches shot in at the open windows, and the lights and shadows of the clouds came and went with the rest of the company. The scent of the flowers, and indeed, of everything that was growing for miles and miles, was most delicious.

Katie was returning to London, and Mamie was going with her for a stay. Dickens had an intense dislike of and a shrinking away from all leave-takings – he never used the word "good-bye" if he could help it, and generally left us for any short absence with a kiss or a nod. Respectful of this, Katie had told Georgina to give her father her love, but as she stood on the porch waiting for the carriage to take her to the station, she must have been seized with an overwhelming desire to see him again, for she hurried across the lawn, through the tunnel, up the wooden staircase to the upper room which was our summer study.

I stretched up from my sunny spot on the writing table to greet Katie as she entered. My Master's head was bent low down over his work, and he turned an eager and rather flushed face towards her. On ordinary occasions he would just have raised his cheek for her kiss, saying a few words, perhaps, in his little language that he had been accustomed to use when she was a child. But on this morning, when he saw her, he pushed his chair from the writing table, opened his arms and took her into them, saying:

"God bless you, Katie!" And there among the branches of trees, among the birds and butterflies, and scent of flowers, his daughter left him.

The next day, Tuesday the 7th of June, my Master returned from an afternoon's walk to find awaiting him the Chinese lanterns he had ordered from London. He, Georgina and I strung them in the conservatory; I, of course, bullying the string, looping it among the scented vines and scarlet geraniums to the delight and consternation of my more purposeful companions.

After dinner we spent the whole evening in the dining room gazing into the conservatory, watching the twinkling lights of the lanterns as they dipped and danced on their strings in the warm, pungent air currents. Dickens sat deep in thought, the fingers of his left hand curled against his cheek, those of his right hand stroking me in his lap.

"That very odd small boy certainly latched on to a splendid notion, did he not, Georgina? Be very persevering, work hard and Gad's Hill might be his some day, might be mine some day. And so it is! How wise my father was in that. My childhood dream has been bountifully fulfilled. Such happy days we have had here. My family has grown up and gone out into the world from this little red-brick house. While I live and, yes, even after, I wish my name to be more and more associated with the place. And when I die, I should like to lie in the little graveyard belonging to Rochester Cathedral at the foot of the Castle Wall."

Rochester Cathedral

Georgina must have admonished her brother-in-law not to dwell just yet on a burial place, for Dickens reached out his hand to reassure her. "Do not be alarmed, Georgina. I still have much to do; I must tangle and untangle the plot threads of intrigue in *The Mystery of Edwin Drood*. My readers depend upon me; I cannot disappoint them. If Puss could speak, he would tell you how rapidly the story advances now. He is my helpmate; why, he would most obligingly tangle and untangle, or perhaps tangle and tangle, those plot threads." As he said this, my Master took my head in both his hands and, working his thumbs back and forth on my cheeks, smiled. "Why, you've been at it so long, you could write a story yourself, if you wanted to; couldn't you, dear Puss?"

We sat together a little while longer; and then my Master rose and, settling me in the warmth of his chair, bade me good-night.

In the early sunshine of the next morning, 8 June, my Master and I were off across the front lawn, down through the cool tunnel and up the steps to our chalet writing room.

Dickens was in excellent spirits. He threw open the chalet windows, gazed out on the sparkling, verdant Kent countryside, and then settled to write Chapter 23 of his mystery.

Contrary to his usual habit, my Master wrote all day, returning to the house with me at his heels only for lunch. After enjoying a cigar in the

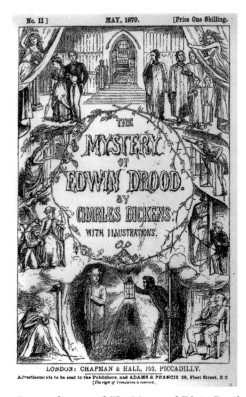

Cover of a part of *The Mystery of Edwin Drood*

conservatory and taking intense delight in that sun-dappled "improve-ment," he strode, albeit with a limp, back to the chalet. In anticipation of the afternoon in his private company, I alternately cavorted ahead, circled round and brought up the rear.

Once in our eyrie, I settled on the writing-desk with my front paws tucked under my chest. Well pleased with this companionable position, I watched the goose-quill pen fairly fly across pages, filling one after another with paragraphs of blue ink. Words had always been my Master's swift messengers, and this day they came to him and did his bidding at once.

Mesmerized by the flicking feather, my eyes slanted shut, and I dozed off and on. Late in the afternoon I lifted my head to see my Master standing at the window, his eyes gazing through the tree-tops toward Rochester Cathedral. He stood thus for quite a while, then returned to his writing-desk, lifted his pen and wrote, speaking the words as they flowed from him:

> "Changes of glorious light from moving boughs, songs of birds, scents from gardens, woods and fields – or, rather, from the one great garden of the whole cultivated island in its yielding time – penetrate into the Cathedral, subdue its earthy odour, and preach the Resur-rection and the Life. The cold stone tombs of centuries ago grow warm; and flecks of brightness dart into the sternest marble corners of the building, fluttering there like wings."

After another page and a half Dickens laid down his pen and reached forward to stroke my chin. I uncurled a paw, and he took it in his hand.

"The little paw that has put out the candle, lo, these many years – ten years 9 June. Why, tomorrow is your birthday, Puss. Bless you, my dear companion," and he gathered me up gently and carried me down the chalet steps. Before we reached the tunnel, the Master of Gad's Hill paused to gaze across the high road at his little mansion of dull red brick with its little weathercock-surmounted cupola on the roof, and a bell hanging in it.

"As I draw closer and closer to the end, I travel in the circle, nearer and nearer to the beginning."

★ ★ ★ ★ ★

The next hours I relate with great difficulty, for they witnessed the end of a noble life.

It was when they were seated at the dinner table that a striking change in the colour and expression of my Master's face startled Georgina. She must have asked if he were ill, for he answered:

"Yes, very ill; I have been very ill for the last hour." Her inclination was to send for a physician, but he forbade her, saying he would go on with dinner. He struggled against the seizure which was fast coming over him and continued to talk but incoherently and very indistinctly. Alarmed, Georgina rose to help him lie down.

"Yes, on the ground," he murmured; and he slipped from her arms to the floor. I paced back and forth beside him and then took my place at his right hand. If it could but reach out and touch me! But it was still.

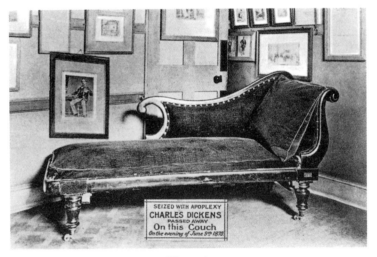

The end

Georgina calmed the distraught servants and had them bring a couch, on which they gently laid Dickens. She dispatched a messenger for the local physician and sent telegrams to the children. Katie and Mamie arrived within hours.

All through the night we watched him – Katie on one side of the couch, Georgina on the other, Mamie keeping hot bricks to the feet which nothing could warm, and I crouched close by on his dinner table chair, hoping and praying that he might open his eyes and look at us, and know us once again. But he never moved, never opened his eyes, never showed a sign of consciousness through all the long night.

A sombre 9 June enfolded the house. Charley arrived in the morning, as did close friends. Georgina summoned Ellen Ternan. The servants murmured prayers and wept. He, whose mere presence in their sick rooms had been a healing influence, could not be healed.

I kept my vigil, but for me the house held a terrible silence now. A sudden gloom had fallen upon the place, and everything was changed; only the still-warm weather continued the same, and the sweet scent of the flowers he had so much admired floated in through the open doors of the conservatory.

My Master lingered through the day, and then a little before six his breathing grew laboured and then diminished. He began to sob and at ten minutes after six, I saw a shudder pass over him. He heaved a deep sigh. A tear rose to his right eye and rolled down his cheek.

At that instant his spirit left us. Silence was all.

So it was that my Master, Charles Dickens, died on 9 June, 1870, amid the peace and beauty of a summer evening in the house he loved. The next day, instead of closing the curtains, as was the custom, to darken the room where my Master lay, Georgina opened them wide to let the afternoon sun stream in. Caught and refracted by the room's looking-glass walls, the light swept in as on angel wings of bright mirror-glass. And as if to complete her girlhood teasing prophecy to her father, Katie placed on the table next to his head a bowl of red geraniums.

Epilogue

When my vigil was over, the flag was lowered for the last time from the mast atop the house, and the simple oak coffin bearing my Master left Gad's Hill. It did not travel the short distance to Rochester Cathedral. No, it journeyed by special train from Higham to Charing Cross Station, London. From there it was drawn in a little funeral cortege to Westminster Abbey, coronation seat and burial place of kings and queens.

Although Charles Dickens had wished to be buried without pomp and ceremony in Kent, he belonged to all of England. Rag-man and royalty, alike, grieved at word of his death. Queen Victoria telegraphed from Balmoral "her deepest regret at the sad news." A working man, coming into a tobacco shop out of a street of mourners, threw his twopence for his purchase on the counter and said simply, "Charles Dickens is dead. We have lost our best friend." Children stopped their street games at the news, and the little daughter of a Covent Garden porter cried, "Dickens is dead? Will Father Christmas die?" The London *Times* called for this son of England to be buried in the country's place of honour.

> Statesmen, men of science, philanthropists, the acknowledged benefactors of their race might pass away, and yet not leave the void which will be caused by the death of Dickens. . .Indeed, such a position is attained by not even one man in an age. It needs an extraordinary combination of intellectual and moral qualities. . .before the world will consent to enthrone a man as their unassailable and enduring favourite. This is the position which Mr. Dickens has occupied with the English and also with the American public for the third of a century. . .Westminster Abbey is the peculiar resting place of English literary genius; and among those whose sacred dust lies there, or whose names are recorded on the walls, very few are

The grave was kept open for two days

Poet's Corner and his gravestone

more worthy than Charles Dickens of such a home. Fewer still, we believe, will be regarded with more honour as time passes, and his greatness grows upon us.

So the family consented, and on 14 June with the great bell tolling, the cortege entered the Abbey's western cloister door, and my Master was carried to Poets' Corner. There, attended only by his family and closest friends, Charles Dickens was laid to rest among the great.

For three days the grave was left open to allow the public to pay tribute. And pay tribute they did. By the thousands they came in silence and in tears, bearing flowers to place on the plain coffin. It was heaped high with all the bright colours and sweet scents my Master so loved: garlands of roses, bunches of daisies gathered by children, small nosegays from country hedgerows, and rough gleanings tied with bits of rags. Down through the decades, they continue to be placed on the simple stone bearing his name. Even today, over a hundred years later, single flowers or small bouquets are left there by admiring and affectionate readers.

Mrs Bouncer in retirement

128

Although it seemed as if the Master of Gad's Hill might at any moment come striding into the house from his daily rounds, or close the Study door behind a morning's writing, or yet sit of an evening by the light of a single candle, he was gone from us. Thus, the family decided to sell the house at auction.

Arrangements were made, with special care taken of the surviving animals. Toby, Trotty Veck, and Boy went to neighbouring freeholds with green pastures. Don and Bumble went to live with Lord Darnley in the Cobham Park they had roamed on their walks with their master. Linda would remain at Gad's, for she had died a summer earlier and had been buried by her master under a great cedar in the garden. I was to go to London with Georgina and Mamie to live in a townhouse. My companion there for play and comfort would be Mrs Bouncer, who now seemed quite my size.

★ ★ ★ ★ ★

At summer's end after our last walk together through the gardens and meadow, Harry and I sat in the evening quiet of the Study, a candle flickering between us on the table. For a long time my companion said nothing. Just once more I wanted a voice to speak to me, so I thought

Henry, aged 21

to share my trick with my Master's beloved son. I lifted my paw and with the quickness of past youth and the grace of present age, I snuffed out the candle.

"So that's how it happens. Father always delighted in telling us of your clever trick, Puss. Now I see it for myself." With that Harry lifted me onto his lap. I tucked my front paws under my chest, and he rolled his fingers under my chin, just as his father, my Master, had done. "We can keep him with us, dear Puss, by remembering him. There is no farewell here. Why, even when he said it himself at his last reading, much as he disliked farewells, it did not, will not, last. Do you know about that evening, Puss? I expect not; how could you? Well, I will tell you the story of it.

"It was the occasion of his Farewell Reading in St. James's Hall in January 1870. His health had been failing for some months past; his readings had been peremptorily stopped by his doctor, but on this occasion he was not to be denied. He read the *Christmas Carol* and the

The farewell reading

Trial from *Pickwick* to a crowded and brilliant audience, and I remember we all thought at the time that he had surpassed himself.

"The solemn and pathetic moment came, however, when he shut his book, and, in the dead silence of the hall, said – alluding to the forthcoming publication of *Edwin Drood* – 'In but two short weeks from this time I hope that you may enter in your own homes on a new series at which my assistance will be indispensable; but from these garish lights I vanish now for evermore with a heartfelt, grateful, respectful, affectionate farewell.'

"When he ceased to speak, a kind of sigh seemed to come from the audience, followed almost at once by such a storm of cheering as I have never heard equalled in my life. He moved from the platform, but the thunderous applause halted him and brought him back. His cheeks wet, he kissed his hand to the audience and left his beloved stage, never to return. But he never leaves us. Not as long as we can talk about him and tell his story. And he never leaves his readers. Not as long as they pick up his books, surround themselves with his host of characters and venture into their worlds.

"Now, once more, Puss. I will light the candle and you can put it out." I rose and stepped from Harry's lap to the table as he struck the match to the wick. Before I lifted my paw, I gazed round the room. In the flickering light, I saw Pip, David, Oliver, Nicholas, Little Dorrit, Scrooge, Fagin and all the glorious company step from the bookshelves and go about the business of their lives. Seated on Harry's knee, which now became once again my Master's knee, was Little Nell looking up at her creator. I caught and held this vision, and then with a salute as of old, I put out the candle.

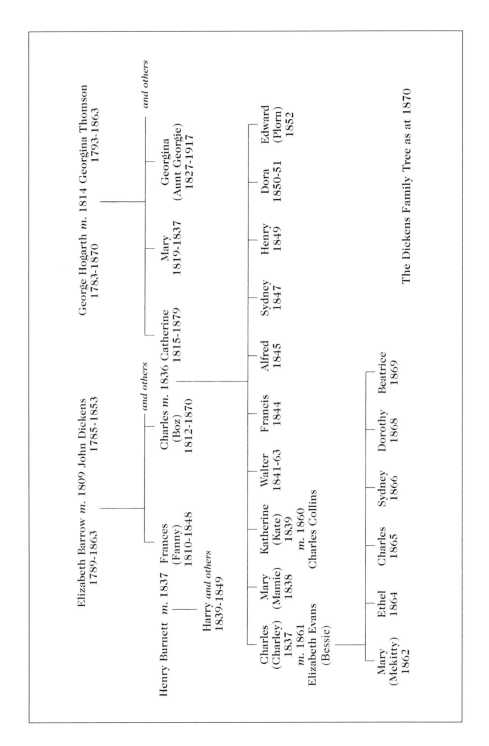

The Dickens Family Tree as at 1870

The Harley School Library